Industrial Cybersecurity Case Studies and Best Practices

Also by Steve Mustard

Author

Mission Critical Operations Primer

Reviews

"This author definitely has long term and recent real world experience and is not a typical cybersecurity academic. New and experienced people will benefit from taking the time to read this."

"If you are looking for a resource in ICS, this book is very thorough."

"One of the better books on OT security, the writer shows an in-depth understanding of the various topics covered. If OT security is your profession, I suggest everyone to read it."

Contributor to

Water Environment Federation, *Design of Water Resource Recovery Facilities, Manual of Practice No. 8*, Sixth Edition

Industrial Cybersecurity Case Studies and Best Practices

Steve Mustard, PE, CAP, GICSP

Copyright © 2022 International Society of Automation (ISA)
All rights reserved.

Printed in the United States of America.
Version: 1.0

ISBN-13: 978-1-64331-154-8 (print)
ISBN-13: 978-1-64331-155-5 (ePub)
ISBN-13: 978-1-64331-156-2 (Kindle)

ISA
P.O. Box 12277
Research Triangle Park, NC 27709

Library of Congress Cataloging-in-Publication Data in process

Dedication

To the people who dedicate their lives to the advancement of knowledge and the dissemination of truth to a world inclusive of everyone. To Charlotte, Benjamin, and Toby for their unwavering support as I continue to dedicate my life to this aim.

Contents

Acknowledgments

Throughout my engineering career of more than 30 years, I have been fortunate to work with many people around the world and for that I am forever grateful. This book would not exist without some key individuals.

To Nick Spencely, Majella Fernando, and Simon FitzGerald for their guidance in my early days, which continues to provide the foundation for everything I do today.

To Nick Rogers, for guiding me through my first (and only) management buyout, which led me to so many more opportunities and, ultimately, to this book.

To Neil Tubman and Mark Davison, the two most brilliant minds I have ever come across, for your continued support throughout the years.

To Mike Morrissey, for showing me how to establish great partnerships between staff and volunteers in professional associations and how to achieve positive results in the process.

To Bryan Parker, Clint Bodungen, Scott Keenon, and Andrew Wadsworth for the Bakersfield experience.

To Elizabeth Selvina and Jason Schurmann for all the experiences, doubles, and pies we shared in La Vertiente, Port of Spain, Reading, and Chinchilla.

To Lauren Goodwin, for your support, and the Clase Azul Reposado.

To Ken Nguyen, for the opportunity to work on one of the most exciting and fulfilling projects of my career, and to all my friends on the digital team for making it fun along the way.

To Steve Huffman, Steve Pflantz, Leo Staples, and Mike Marlowe, for your friendship, mentorship, support, and chicken pot pie.

To Blair Traynor, Nicky Jones, John Flynn, and Paul Holland for your invaluable comments on drafts of this book.

To Liegh Elrod, for your never-ending support and never-failing belief that I would one day finish this book, and to all the ISA publications team for all your hard work turning the material into a professional product.

To Andrea Holovach, for supporting me throughout my ISA presidency, reviewing memes, and consistently demonstrating your eligibility for a place on the Ark Fleet Ship A.

To the ISA staff, for working together with the member community to create a better world through automation.

To Bill Furlow, for painstakingly reviewing and fixing my writing, while simultaneously being an expert mixologist, part time bon vivant, and full time Bojack Horseman fan.

Finally, to David Boyle, my friend and colleague for too many years to count. A true friend accepts who you are, but also helps you become who you should be. Thank you for helping me be better.

About the Author

Steve Mustard is an independent automation consultant and a subject matter expert of the International Society of Automation (ISA).

Backed by more than 30 years of engineering experience, Mustard specializes in the development and management of real-time embedded equipment and automation systems. He serves as president of National Automation, Inc., and served as the 2021 president of ISA.

Mustard is a recognized authority on industrial cybersecurity, having developed and delivered cybersecurity management systems, procedures, training, and guidance to various global critical infrastructure organizations.

Mustard is a licensed Professional Engineer in Texas and Kansas, a UK registered Chartered Engineer, a European registered Eur Ing, an ISA Certified Automation Professional (CAP), a certified Global Industrial Cybersecurity Professional (GICSP), and a Certified Mission Critical Professional. He also is a Fellow in the Institution of Engineering and Technology (IET), a Senior Member of ISA, a member of the Safety and Security Committee of the Water Environment Federation (WEF), a board member of the Mission Critical Global Alliance (MCGA), and a member of the American Water Works Association (AWWA).

Mustard writes and presents on a wide array of technical topics and is the author of *Mission Critical Operations Primer*, published by ISA. He has also contributed to other technical books, including the Water Environment Federation's *Design of Water Resource Recovery Facilities, Manual of Practice No.8*, sixth edition.

1

Introduction

"I'm The Creeper: Catch Me If You Can."[1]

With no malicious intent, Bob Thomas created the first computer worm, called *Creeper*. That was quickly followed by Ray Thomlinson's *Reaper*, designed to find Creeper and shut it down; in essence, it was the first antivirus program. This was the early 1970s, 15 years before Windows 1.0 was released and 19 years before Tim Berners-Lee coined the term *World Wide Web*.

Windows would eventually come to dominate the operating system market and, as a result, be the primary target for malicious attacks. During this period, control system vendors began moving their software from operating systems such as Unix to Windows. This move allowed them to benefit from standardization and improved time to market.

By 2000, the benefits of integrating control systems with the enterprise were being realized, and the ISA-95 standard ("Enterprise-Control System Integration") articulated these benefits with a clear definition of how to achieve them. At this point, Google had been around for two years, Amazon was only six years old, and e-commerce in the United States made up just 1% of retail sales. That same year, the ILOVEYOU worm infected an estimated 50 million computers, causing more than $5.5 billion in damage.

---

1 George Dalakov, "The First Computer Virus of Bob Thomas (Complete History)," accessed July 25, 2021, https://history-computer.com/inventions/the-first-computer-virus-of-bob-thomas-complete-history/.

From the early 2000s, when Vitek Boden used a stolen laptop and a radio to wreak havoc at a sewage treatment plant in Queensland, Australia; through 2010, when the Stuxnet malware disrupted production at an Iranian nuclear enrichment facility; to 2018, when attackers gained access to safety systems and shut down a Middle East refinery, the threats of malware and cyberattacks have increased in lockstep with advances in industrial automation.

Conventional cybersecurity for business systems and personal computers constantly evolved to keep up with the growing threat from malware. By contrast, the universal acceptance that industrial control and automation systems were vulnerable to such threats has taken much longer to sink in. In fact, 20 years later, many fail to recognize the threat, much less the need for action.

The discipline of industrial automation and control systems cybersecurity (*industrial cybersecurity* for short) is still in its infancy. An international standard exists. There are various guides and a small number of sector-specific regulations; however, although the "what" is clearly defined, the "how" is still being developed.

Some industry sectors have progressed further than others. Some sectors, such as oil and gas, have invested heavily in industrial cybersecurity. Other sectors, such as water and wastewater, remain behind the curve on addressing their cybersecurity. In all cases, asset owners/operators have largely developed their own solutions and systems in isolation. This results in similar approaches with varying degrees of success.

Two distinct cybersecurity professions have emerged: information technology (IT) cybersecurity, concerned with information security, personal information, and financial transactions; and operational technology (OT) cybersecurity, concerned with operational system availability and safety. Some say there should be no distinction between IT and OT cybersecurity, whereas others believe the unique operational nature of each environment necessitates such a distinction.

Whether or not there is a distinction, one thing is clear: cybersecurity is a major risk for any business or entity. A report from the 2019 RSA[2] Conference notes that cybersecurity spending has increased 141% since 2010. In 2019, worldwide spending on

---

2 RSA is an acronym made up of the first letters of the last names of the three company co-founders: Ron Rivest, Adi Shamir, and Leonard Adleman.

cybersecurity was estimated to reach over $124 billion.[3] Gartner is forecasting this spend to reach $150 billion in 2021.[4] Despite this increase in spending, the number of incidents and their impact have grown even faster. Data from Cybersecurity Ventures forecasts the worldwide cost of ransomware damage in 2021 to be $20 billion, 57 times higher than it was in 2015.[5] RiskBased Security's 2020 year-end data breach report showed that the number of data records compromised in 2020 exceeded 37 billion, a 141% increase compared to 2019.[6]

Although the number of OT-specific cybersecurity incidents remains low, we should not be complacent. Awareness of industrial control systems is growing with each new incident. These incidents reveal a lack of preparedness by asset owners and present attractive targets to organized crime syndicates and nation-states. Even a disgruntled former employee or contractor may recognize an opportunity for revenge.

During the final stage of writing this book, four OT-related cybersecurity incidents occurred. The first, in February 2021, occurred when an unauthorized remote access user tampered with the levels of a toxic chemical in a water treatment plant.[7] The second incident, reported a month later, occurred in 2019 and was initiated by a disgruntled former employee who attempted to remotely tamper with a different water treatment plant.[8] In the third incident, a fuel pipeline was shut down for a week after the company's billing system was incapacitated by ransomware.[9] The fourth incident, also involving ransomware, occurred two weeks later, impacting the operations of a global meat producer. The company paid an $11 million ransom and was able to restore operations in less than one week.[10] Some experts distinguished the two

---

3 RSAC Contributor, "The Future of Companies and Cybersecurity Spending," accessed June 21, 2021, https://www.rsaconference.com/library/Blog/the-future-of-companies-and-cybersecurity-spending.

4 Gartner, "Gartner Forecasts Worldwide Security and Risk Management Spending to Exceed $150 Billion in 2021," May 17, 2021, accessed June 21, 2021, https://www.gartner.com/en/newsroom/press-releases/2021-05-17-gartner-forecasts-worldwide-security-and-risk-managem.

5 Finances Online, "119 Impressive Cybersecurity Statistics: 2020/2021 Data & Market Analysis," accessed June 21, 2021, https://financesonline.com/cybersecurity-statistics/.

6 RiskBased Security, "2020 Year End Report: Data Breach QuickView," accessed June 21, 2021, https://pages.riskbasedsecurity.com/en/en/2020-yearend-data-breach-quickview-report.

7 Jack Evans, "Someone Tried to Poison Oldsmar's Water Supply during Hack, Sheriff Says," *Tampa Bay Times*, February 9, 2021, accessed June 21, 2021, https://www.tampabay.com/news/pinellas/2021/02/08/someone-tried-to-poison-oldsmars-water-supply-during-hack-sheriff-says/.

8 Chris Young, "A 22-Year-Old Logged in and Compromised Kansas's Water System Remotely," Interesting Engineering website, April 6, 2021, accessed June 21, 2021, https://interestingengineering.com/a-22-year-old-logged-in-and-compromised-kansas-water-system-remotely.

9 Ellen Nakashima, Yeganeh Torbati, and Will Englund, "Ransomware Attack Leads to Shutdown of Major US Pipeline System," *Washington Post*, May 8, 2021, accessed June 21, 2021, https://www.washingtonpost.com/business/2021/05/08/cyber-attack-colonial-pipeline/.

10 Jacob Bunge, "JBS Paid $11 Million to Resolve Ransomware Attack," *Wall Street Journal*, June 9, 2021, accessed June 21, 2021, https://www.wsj.com/articles/jbs-paid-11-million-to-resolve-ransomware-attack-11623280781.

ransomware incidents as IT, not OT, cyberattacks. Although this is technically correct, the result was indistinguishable from an OT attack. The pipeline control system was disabled, and operations were shut down. This led to panic buying and gas shortages across the southeastern United States. There was further potential for interruption of critical services, such as airports, that depend on this fuel supply. The meat producer shutdown could have led to similar issues had it not been resolved as quickly as it was. In short, we are, on the whole, woefully unprepared to adequately manage cybersecurity incidents, be they IT or OT.

This book examines all aspects of industrial cybersecurity, beginning with an analysis of the differences between IT and OT cybersecurity. Understanding these differences is essential to a successful industrial cybersecurity program. Also essential to a successful program is governance. An effective industrial cybersecurity management system must first be established. Recognizing this is a process fraught with difficulty, the book will offer tips on overcoming the challenges.

Industrial cybersecurity is all about quantifying and managing risk. This book provides practical methods to ensure cybersecurity risk is clearly understood throughout the organization.

Addressing industrial cybersecurity risks includes several key elements, but the foundation is good system design. This book will provide guidance to define secure additions and modifications for brownfield sites as well as secure-by-design solutions for greenfield sites.

Poor project delivery can negate some or all of the benefits of secure designs. This can take the form of poor execution or oversight. It might entail the introduction of new vulnerabilities that are not properly identified or addressed. It can even be seen in poor practices during the development or commissioning of a system. This book will provide some guidance on effective oversight methods.

The need to raise and maintain awareness in personnel is not unique to industrial cybersecurity. That goes for everyone on staff, from senior management, who provides the funding and own the risk; to the frontline workers, who are most likely to be involved in either causing or avoiding an incident. This book will offer tips on raising awareness of the risks and strategies to manage them.

Finally, this book will consider the role operational support plays in industrial cybersecurity. That includes day-to-day activities such as operating system patching and system backups, as well as preparation for and response to cybersecurity incidents.

About this Book

There are thousands of books on the subject of cybersecurity. Many address areas of cybersecurity such as ethical hacking, attack and defense strategies, and secure architectures. A minority of books speak to the development of cybersecurity programs and cybersecurity risk. Even fewer examine the cultural aspects. Very few books specifically cover industrial cybersecurity.

There are three core elements of cybersecurity: people, process, and technology. Industrial cybersecurity is distinct from its counterpart in the IT world, encompassing not just technology, but also the broader elements related to people and processes.

With this in mind, the aim is to provide an understanding of the objectives, and how to achieve them, without being prescriptive on technical details.

This book is based on my 30 plus years of industrial experience involving projects in various countries and sectors, including almost 20 years of addressing cybersecurity issues. During 2005, in a secure building on the banks of the river Thames, a meeting of the United Kingdom's National Infrastructure Security Coordination Centre (now called the Centre for the Protection of National Infrastructure—CPNI) was convened to discuss information sharing for the United Kingdom's critical national infrastructure. One topic of discussion at that meeting was *how to get vendors to promptly approve critical security patches*. Almost 20 years later, I still hear similar discussions. By and large, vendors are still not providing the resources needed to preapprove patches for release. There is a tendency to say most, if not all, of the responsibility lies with the asset owner.

A whole industry has grown around cybersecurity, including a sector dedicated to OT environments. And yet, today there are still vendors who claim their solution will not work if antivirus software is installed. We see asset owners deploying insecure products, and users continuing to perform insecure actions. Some asset owners deploy expensive, complex tool sets for network monitoring and asset management. It does them little good when they lack accurate documentation to make effective use of these tools. These same asset owners have huge gaps in their cybersecurity management controls—the kinds of gaps that cause the most basic incident to halt production, damage equipment, injure people, and harm the environment.

This book is intended to help identify these gaps and offer solutions to address them. I focus on the highest risk areas that can be tackled immediately with the least additional cost and effort.

I sincerely hope that we can make more progress going forward than we have in the past 20 years. And I hope this book can contribute to that progress.

Terminology

Cybersecurity, like many technical subjects, comes with its own lexicon and, with that, many confusing and interchangeable terms.

There are ongoing debates about the most appropriate and inclusive terms for the subject matter of this book. I have used the term *industrial cybersecurity*, but I acknowledge that some sectors or specialisms consider themselves excluded. For example, many building automation system providers and users do not typically consider themselves as "industrial."

Operational technology, or OT, is another term that has been created to attempt to distinguish industrial environments from information technology, or IT, environments. Even this term generates discussion, and what is included or excluded often depends on interpretation. Some even suggest that there is no distinction; there is only technology.

Even the definition of automation systems is hotly debated. The ISA/IEC 62443 Series of Standards, which will be referenced throughout this book, is titled *Security for Industrial Automation and Control Systems*. The abbreviation for industrial automation and control systems, IACSs, is frequently used interchangeably with ICSs (industrial control systems). *Cyber physical systems* is another term that is gaining traction.

The series title brings up a final terminology question: Should the term used be "cybersecurity" or simply "security"? Some believe that the cyber distinction leads to incorrect assumptions such as this: ownership of the risk lies with an organization's chief information security officer (CISO). Others have accepted that the term *cybersecurity* has been adopted sufficiently and that changing it would lead to further confusion.

Throughout this book I will use many of these terms, sometimes interchangeably. However, I believe the ideas in this book apply equally well to any system or electronic and computing parts used to monitor and control physical processes, whether they be in an industrial facility, a commercial building, a vehicle, or anywhere else.

Intended Audience

This book is intended for anyone involved in industrial automation and control systems cybersecurity, including operators, technicians, engineers, and managers within asset-owner and asset-operator organizations; product vendors; system integrators; and consultants.

2

What Makes Industrial Cybersecurity Different?

Introduction

Information technology (IT) cybersecurity is concerned with information security, personal information, and financial transactions. Operational technology (OT) cybersecurity is concerned with operational system availability and safety.

One school of thought says there should be no distinction between IT and OT cybersecurity. Its mantra: Technology is technology. The use of IT products in industrial control systems has increased dramatically in the past 40 years. Systems now run on servers and workstations running Windows operating systems and databases. These systems have many IT-oriented application layer protocols in use. However, the use of that technology and the consequences when it fails are distinct.

This chapter highlights key differences between OT and IT environments. It looks at how cybersecurity practices must adapt to cope with these differences.

What Are the Differences between OT and IT?

Relative Priorities

The conventional answer to the question "Why is industrial cybersecurity different?" was based on the C-I-A (confidentiality-integrity-availability) triad and the different priorities for IT and OT environments. This was a good starting point. It provided some clarity to those unfamiliar with industrial automation systems. The triad also helped cybersecurity experts realize that confidentiality is not the only consideration when addressing risk.

Availability is a factor for IT systems, but there is some confusion about the importance of availability. To address possible misunderstandings, a fourth element, safety, began appearing in the OT priorities.

The C-I-A/S triad is a helpful tool. However, more clarity is needed to improve the understanding of what sets industrial cybersecurity apart.

The Golden Triangle

Although it is true that "technology is technology," technology is only one-third of the cybersecurity golden triangle, as shown in Figure 2-1.

Table 2-1 summarizes the key differences between IT and OT environments for these three elements.

To date, the focus on IT/OT differences has been on the technology element. Many books and presentations have discussed similar lists of differences. These differences continue to be important:

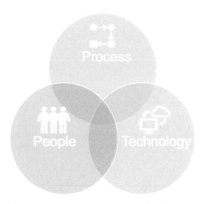

Figure 2-1. The golden triangle of people, process, and technology.

Table 2-1. Summary of people, process, and technology differences.

	IT	OT
People	• Primary focus is the service provision • Underlying technology is the majority of the service • Control and management of data • Many skilled professionals	• Primary focus is safety, then production • Underlying technology is a means to an end • Control and management of physical processes • Limited pool of skilled professionals
Process	• Agile, flexible • Frequently undocumented • Risks assessed during procurement; limited assessment prior to updates • IT cybersecurity process is mature	• Rigid, enforced • Documented in standard operating procedures • Risks assessed before any maintenance or changes made • OT cybersecurity process is emerging and evolving
Technology	• Frequently updated • IT, network, and cybersecurity tool integration supported • Lower environmental standards and reliability acceptable • Stochastic processes with variable response times	• Rarely updated; only if necessary • Limited support for IT, network, and cybersecurity tool integration • Rugged environmental standards and high reliability required • Deterministic processes requiring real-time interaction

- The frequency of technology refresh is unlikely to change in OT environments. The technology is there to support a high-availability production system. The adage "if it ain't broke, don't fix it" is common in OT environments. Taking systems out of service to perform updates is not only costly, but it also introduces new risks: New technology has less of a track record and includes additional features that may create unexpected consequences. Consider Boeing's 737 MAX 800 aircraft, which entered service in 2017. After two fatal crashes, the aircraft was grounded in 2019. One factor in the crashes was the introduction of a new automated flight control system called Maneuvering Characteristics Augmentation System (MCAS), which was not explained in any manuals or in crew training.[11]

- Although newer OT systems include some components that will integrate with IT, network, or cybersecurity tools, they may never include full support across all components. Some components, such as safety controllers, must minimize their functionality to maximize performance and reliability. In addition, segregation using protocol firewalls will limit the ability to reach devices using IT

---

11 Jon Hemmerdinger, "Boeing Asked FAA in 2017 to Strip MCAS from Max Training Report," FlightGlobal website, October 18, 2019, accessed June 21, 2021, https://www.flightglobal.com/air-framers/boeing-asked-faa-in-2017-to-strip-mcas-from-max-training-report/134896.article.

tools. More importantly, because of the long life cycle already mentioned, many facilities will continue to run on legacy equipment that cannot support such integration.

- The server and workstation elements of OT systems have converged with their IT equivalents in terms of environmental standards and reliability. This is possible because these items operate in climate-controlled environments. There are many elements of OT systems that will continue to operate in harsh environments and will always need specialist hardware.

To date, there has been less focus on the people and process elements—specifically, their impact on IT/OT differences. These elements can be summed up in four distinct points:

1. The significance of technology

2. The significance of culture

3. Consequences

4. Mitigations

The Significance of Technology

Figure 2-2 shows an example of typical elements of IT and OT projects.

Consider the replacement of a billing system as a typical IT project. The project will involve the purchase of new hardware and software, data migration, some customization work, and project management. The cybersecurity funding will be distributed

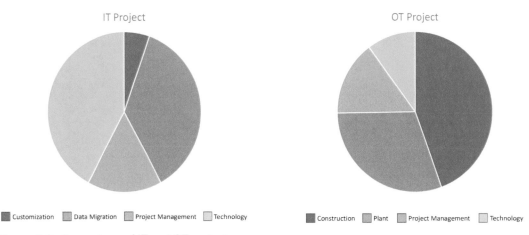

Figure 2-2. Proportions of IT and OT projects.

across the technology, data migration, and customization portions of the budget as applicable. Although the actual proportions may vary, the IT project example in Figure 2-2 is indicative of the vast majority of projects that revolve around technology. This is understandable because the project success hinges entirely on delivering the technology.

Now, consider a typical OT project involving the construction of a new manufacturing plant or other production facility. In this case, the balance shifts toward construction-related elements: the plant itself and the facility to house it. The technology element is now a minor part of the overall project. As a result, it gets less attention. Even the safety system, critical to the protection of the facility, personnel, and the environment, is usually only 1% to 2% of the project budget.[12] Security, if there is any, will be even less prominent within the technology portion of the budget. The total cost of ownership over the asset life, including managing the security controls, is considered to be someone else's problem. Yet decisions made during the project phase have a significant impact on this cost.

As with the IT example, the proportions may vary from project to project, but the emphasis on the plant and facility at the expense of technology and security will be similar in each project. This tendency will have ramifications on contracts, procurement, planning, and resource priorities. All these factors can have a negative impact on the resulting security of the facility.

Because they tend to include significant construction elements, OT projects run for many years. A complete OT project to build a new oil and gas production platform may take more than 10 years from feasibility to start-up. Much can change in this time, especially in the technology area. Such changes have a subsequent impact on cybersecurity.

The impact of OT projects on cybersecurity is discussed further in Chapter 6, "Pitfalls of Project Delivery."

The attention paid to technology is directly proportional to its percentage of the scope and budget (see Figure 2-2). And because cybersecurity is only a part of the technology element, it will get even less attention. As a result, cybersecurity issues are unlikely to rise to a level of importance that could impact project or operational activities. This will be discussed more in later chapters.

---

12 S. Lucchini, "I Thought I Had the Right Roadmap for Implementing a Safety System!," (white paper presented at the Texas A&M Engineering Experiment Station, 20th Annual International Symposium, Mary Kay O'Connor Process Safety Center, Texas A&M University, 2017).

The Significance of Culture

IT and OT cultures are vastly different. IT has fully embraced the agile methodology that is based on self-organizing teams and iterative development methods. The traditional waterfall method of defining requirements, development, and verification has been replaced by DevOps (a combination of software development and operations). DevOps aims to shorten the development life cycle and encourages continuous change. There is an intentional *experimental* aspect to DevOps. Teams are encouraged to *fail-fast*, that is, to try something to determine if it works. If it fails, move on and try something else.

By contrast, the OT culture resists change as this impacts production and introduces unnecessary risk. OT-focused organizations emphasize safety culture as their number one priority.

The term *safety culture* was first introduced in 1986 after the Chernobyl nuclear accident. In this incident, the core of reactor number 4 at the Chernobyl Nuclear Power Plant in Pripyat, Ukraine, ruptured in a steam explosion, releasing 5% of the core's radioactive material into the environment.[13] The Chernobyl accident is one of only two nuclear accidents rated at the maximum severity on the International Nuclear Event Scale.[14] The Chernobyl disaster killed 30 people within weeks and caused an estimated 6,500 cancer cases. It also required the evacuation of 350,000 people. The accident occurred during a safety test that involved simulating a power outage. It resulted from a combination of a flaw in the reactor design and inadequately trained operators.

The UK Health and Safety Commission defines safety culture as follows:

> The product of individual and group values, attitudes, perceptions, competencies, and patterns of behavior that determine the commitment to, and the style and proficiency of, an organization's health and safety management.

Although there is a convergence of IT and OT technology (using common technology platforms and connecting systems), the *fail-fast* approach of modern IT and the risk-averse safety culture of OT will never, and should never, converge. So, it is essential that this consideration is factored into an effective industrial cybersecurity management system. The current cybersecurity culture in OT environments is not dissimilar to the safety culture of the late 1980s, where bad practices were prevalent and went

---

13 World Nuclear Association, "Chernobyl Accident 1986," accessed June 21, 2021, https://www.world-nuclear.org/information-library/safety-and-security/safety-of-plants/chernobyl-accident.aspx.

14 The other occurred at the Fukushima Daiichi Nuclear Power Plant in Ōkuma, Japan, and was caused by an earthquake and subsequent tsunami.

unaddressed. Reducing industrial cybersecurity risk to tolerable levels will require the same level of focus that has been applied to industrial safety.

Consequences

One of the biggest challenges that OT cybersecurity specialists have faced is distinguishing the consequences of failure in OT systems from their IT counterparts.

As already noted, the C-I-A triad greatly simplifies the relative concerns for IT and OT systems. A more realistic list of potential consequences is as follows:

- **Privacy violation** – Exfiltration of personally identifiable information (PII), such as government identification numbers and bank account numbers

- **Operational impact** – Loss of production capacity, inability to process customer orders, and other effects

- **Reputational damage** – Typically related to another consequence, such as privacy violation, environmental harm, injury, or loss of life

- **Regulatory impact** – Typically related to another consequence, such as operational impact, environmental harm, injury, or loss of life

- **Injury or loss of life** – Harm to workers in the operational environment or to members of the public, for instance, from fire or explosion

- **Environmental harm** – Release of pollutants or other harmful materials into a body of water or the atmosphere

The consequences of IT system failure are easy to comprehend; for instance, most people can understand the implications of having their PII stolen. There have been many high-profile cybersecurity incidents with these such consequences.

In 2013, hackers gained access to Target's computer network using credentials stolen from a third-party vendor.[15] The attackers "gained access to a customer service database, installed malware on the system and captured full names, phone numbers, email

---

15 The vendor, Fazio Mechanical Services, provided heating, ventilation, and air conditioning (HVAC) services to Target. It was the subject of a phishing attack that resulted in the exfiltration of credentials for Target's billing system. The attackers used this system to gain access to the rest of Target's network. Because HVAC was indirectly involved, many mistakenly believe that this attack was the result of ingress via a less-secure HVAC network. Brian Krebs, "Target Hackers Broke in Via HVAC Company," KrebsOnSecurity blog, February 5, 2014, accessed June 21, 2021, https://krebsonsecurity.com/2014/02/target-hackers-broke-in-via-hvac-company/.

addresses, payment card numbers, credit card verification codes, and other sensitive data."[16] In total, contact information for 60 million Target customers, including payment card account data for 41 million customers, was exfiltrated. In a multistate settlement in 2017, Target agreed to pay 47 states and the District of Columbia $18.5 million. The company also agreed to develop a comprehensive information security program and undertake all the activities related to that.

In 2017, the records of over 160 million customers were exfiltrated from credit bureau Equifax. The data included "first and last names, Social Security numbers, birth dates, addresses and, in some instances, driver's license numbers."[17] The incident resulted in major disruption to the credit industry, and Equifax eventually settled with the US Federal Trade Commission, agreeing to pay "$380,500,000 into a fund for class benefits, attorneys' fees, expenses, service awards, and notice and administration costs; up to an additional $125,000,000 if needed to satisfy claims for certain out-of-pocket losses; and potentially $2 billion more if all 147 million class members sign up for credit monitoring."[18]

Given the sheer number of high-profile incidents, the consequences of IT system cybersecurity incidents are easy to comprehend. The same cannot be said for OT systems. Awareness is growing outside OT circles that there are electronic systems that control physical processes and manufacturing systems. The consequences if these systems fail are not as well understood or accepted by those responsible for funding cybersecurity.

Part of the problem is that, unlike IT systems, there have been very few high-profile cybersecurity incidents involving OT systems. This may be misleading. OT environments tend to have less extensive monitoring than IT environments, so malicious activity may be going unnoticed. The tendency for organizations to avoid bad publicity or embarrassment may also play a part in underreporting OT cybersecurity incidents.

Efforts to point out the potential consequences arising from a cybersecurity incident are generally ignored or dismissed. Critics say that OT systems are guarded by other

---

16 Kevin McCoy, "Target to Pay $18.5M for 2013 Data Breach that Affected 41 Million Consumers," *USA Today*, updated May 23, 2017, accessed June 21, 2021, https://www.usatoday.com/story/money/2017/05/23/target-pay-185m-2013-data-breach-affected-consumers/102063932/.

17 "2017 Equifax Data Breach," Wikipedia, accessed June 21, 2021, https://en.wikipedia.org/wiki/2017_Equifax_data_breach.

18 "Order Granting Final Approval of Settlement, Certifying Settlement Class, and Awarding Attorney's Fees, Expenses, and Service Awards," Equifax Data Breach Settlement, accessed June 21, 2021, https://www.equifaxbreachsettlement.com/admin/services/connectedapps.cms.extensions/1.0.0.0/927686a8-4491-4976-bc7b-83cccaa34de0_1033_EFX_Final_Approval_Order_(1.13.2020).pdf.

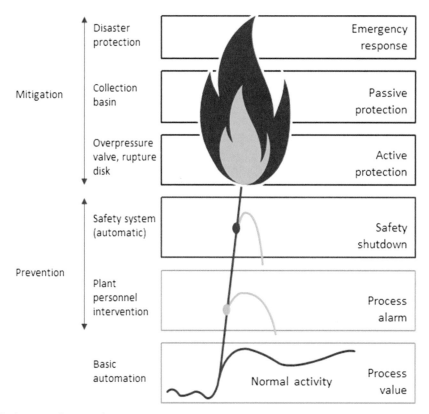

Figure 2-3. Layers of protection.

layers of protection, such as mechanical fail-safe equipment (e.g., overpressure valves, rupture disks). These fail-safes prevent serious consequences such as loss of primary containment, fire, or explosion (as shown in Figure 2-3). Reliance on these fail-safes creates a false sense of security.

The cybersecurity attacks on OT systems to date have demonstrated that the first three layers can be compromised. This means that organizations depend on additional layers of protection to save them from catastrophe:

- **Basic automation layer** – In attacks on three energy distribution companies in the Ukraine, hackers remotely seized control of the supervisory control and data acquisition (SCADA) system, switching substations off. Up to 73 MWh of electricity (or 0.015% of daily electricity consumption in the Ukraine) was interrupted, leaving customers without power for up to six hours.

- **Plant personnel intervention layer** – In the Stuxnet attack, malware was able to push the centrifuges outside their normal operating envelope, while reporting to operators that conditions were normal. The resulting damage to the centrifuges set back the Iranian uranium enrichment program several years.

- **Safety system layer** – In the TRISIS attack, bad actors attempted to replace the code in a safety controller. The attempt was thwarted when the safety system, operating as designed, failed safe, shutting in the plant. Although there was no loss of primary containment or harm to individuals, a plant shut-in is highly undesirable.

The risk assessment of the facility or process is based on the assumption that all layers of protection are in place and will operate on demand. This means organizations must take seriously the threat of a cybersecurity incident on these systems.

Consider the example of a gas turbine control system. Gas turbines are used extensively in industry for critical processes, such as power generation, gas compression, and water injection. A gas turbine is shown in Figure 2-4. A typical gas turbine may cost $6 million (£4.3 million), weigh 20,000 lb (9000 kg), and operate at up to 10,000 psi (69,000 kPa).

A control system is required to safely operate the turbine and shut it down in the event of a serious situation. Figure 2-5 shows a simplified block diagram of this system.

A programmable logic controller (PLC) is the basis for the control functions that provide the *basic automation* layer; a connected human-machine interface (HMI) enables operators to observe the system status and make set-point changes (the *plant personnel intervention* layer).

The safety functions that form the *safety system* layer may include a safety controller that focuses on turbine protection, and a fire and gas controller that interfaces with

Figure 2-4. Gas turbine used for power generation, gas compression, and water injection.

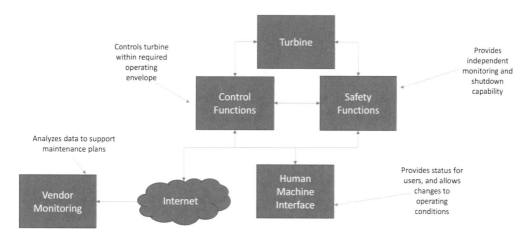

Figure 2-5. Simplified gas turbine control system showing potential cybersecurity risks.

the safety controller to shut down the turbine if required. These functions operate independently of the control functions and react immediately, and automatically, to contain or mitigate a hazard.

To provide warranty and support for the end user, the gas turbine vendor collects process data from the system. This data typically travels over a secure connection between the vendor's operations center and the facility. This connection enables the vendor to analyze turbine performance and determine maintenance actions.

The gas turbine control system is vulnerable to the same incidents discussed earlier:

- The *basic automation* layer can be compromised, enabling the system to be operated remotely. This could result in the turbine being shut down, causing a power failure or loss of production at the facility.

- The *plant personnel intervention* layer can be compromised so that the turbine migrates outside its normal operating envelope (by manipulating the basic automation layer). Meanwhile, it appears to the users at the facility and the vendor to be operating normally. This can cause damage and an unplanned outage, resulting in loss of power or production. The plant will face unplanned repair costs and the challenges of operating without the damaged turbine.

- The *safety system* layer can be compromised so that the automatic shutdown is disabled. This can result in catastrophic damage to the turbine (e.g., after running without lube oil present), power failure, loss of production, fire, or explosion.

As awareness of OT systems grows, the threat to organizations that operate them grows. Nation-states now see potential for major disruption to their enemies through attacks on OT systems. After the Stuxnet attack on Iran's Natanz uranium enrichment facility was made public in 2010, it led to a series of cyberattacks and counterattacks involving the United States, Iran, Saudi Arabia, and Israel. Iranians were indicted in 2016 for attempting to gain access to a US dam system in upstate New York.[19] The Shamoon-related attacks on Saudi Aramco and its vendors, such as Saipem, have been attributed to Iran.[20,21] Israel attacked an Iranian port in May 2020, causing "massive backups on waterways and roads leading to the facility."[22]

At present none of the layers of protection are designed to detect or react to malicious activity. As a result, we must introduce alternate mitigations to manage the risk of cybersecurity incidents affecting these layers of protection.

Mitigations

The response to the cybersecurity threat in IT and OT systems must be distinct.

Consider the example of the gas turbine control system. External access is limited to a secure connection with the vendor's operations center. There is no particular concern regarding sensitive data exfiltration; however, note the following:

- The PLC, HMI, safety controller, and fire and gas controller may be accessed by anyone in the facility. This flaw enables an unauthorized individual to reprogram these systems or deploy malware to the HMI. Although the specialist skills and knowledge to work on these systems can be hard to find, there are several examples of hackers with no industrial control systems experience identifying and exploiting vulnerabilities in those systems. In one example, two hackers with no prior product experience identified three previously unknown

19   Mark Thompson, "Iranian Cyber Attack on New York Dam Shows Future of War, *Time*, March 24, 2016, accessed June 21, 2021, https://time.com/4270728/iran-cyber-attack-dam-fbi/.

20   "FireEye Responds to Wave of Destructive Cyber Attacks in Gulf Region," FireEye blog, December 1, 2016, accessed June 21, 2021, https://www.fireeye.com/blog/threat-research/2016/11/fireeye_respondsto.html.

21   Thomas Brewster, "Warnings as Destructive 'Shamoon' Cyber Attacks Hit Middle East Energy Industry," *Forbes*, December 13, 2018, accessed June 21, 2021, https://www.forbes.com/sites/thomasbrewster/2018/12/13/warnings-as-destructive-shamoon-cyber-attacks-hit-middle-east-energy-industry/#53fe71893e0f.

22   Joby Warrick and Ellen Nakashima, "Officials: Israel Linked to a Disruptive Cyberattack on Iranian Port Facility," *Washington Post*, May 18, 2020, accessed June 21, 2021, https://www.washingtonpost.com/national-security/officials-israel-linked-to-a-disruptive-cyberattack-on-iranian-port-facility/2020/05/18/9d1da866-9942-11ea-89fd-28fb313d1886_story.html.

vulnerabilities in a major automation vendor's product and presented them at the RootedCON 2014.[23,24]

- OT facilities have a variety of physical controls, such as lockable cabinets and rooms, and strict procedures for accessing and working in these areas. Nevertheless, personnel may bypass some of these controls, for example, by leaving cabinets unlocked.

- The turbine control system network may be isolated from the wider network (aside from the vendor connection). This means automated monitoring and updates of Windows equipment may need to be done manually.

- The secure connection provides some protection, but the effectiveness of this control depends on the awareness, training, policies, procedures, and physical security behaviors of the vendor's personnel.

Based on these considerations, the focus on mitigations for the gas turbine control system is distinct from that for mitigations for an IT system in several ways:

- **Physical and electronic security** – Limiting physical and electronic access to the control system components to authorized individuals only. This is accomplished by such actions as locking doors and cabinets and protecting usernames and passwords.

- **Strict enforcement of procedures** – For instance, limiting, or banning, the use of removable media and maintaining security updates, antivirus software, and signatures (or using application control) on Windows equipment.

As noted earlier, the focus is more on the people and the processes than the technology. The misuse or insecure use of technology in the OT environment can create significant vulnerabilities. A safety culture with well-trained people following strict processes and procedures is essential in the OT environment.

---

23 Brian Prince, "Researchers Detail Critical Vulnerabilities in SCADA Product," *Security Week*, March 13, 2014, accessed June 21, 2021, https://www.securityweek.com/researchers-detail-critical-vulnerabilities-scada-product.

24 "Juan Vazquez and Julián Vilas, "A patadas con mi SCADA! [Rooted CON 2014]," YouTube, accessed June 21, 2021, https://www.youtube.com/watch?v=oEwxm8EwtYA&list=PLUOjNfYgonUsrFhtONP7a18451psKNv4I&index=23.

Foundations of Industrial Cybersecurity Management

Having established why industrial cybersecurity is different, let us consider the four key elements of a cybersecurity management system:

- **Governance** – The collective term for the oversight and decision-making required for an effective system

- **Policies and procedures** – The documentation associated with all aspects of the system including personnel security, risk management, access control, system maintenance, and business continuity management

- **Training** – The tools and methods used to raise awareness and to ensure policies and procedures are followed

- **Technical** – The collection of devices, appliances, and analysis tools used to implement cybersecurity controls

As shown in Figure 2-6, governance is the foundation of a cybersecurity management system. Governance in cybersecurity is akin to physiological needs in Abraham Maslow's famous hierarchy of human needs. It forms the base of the pyramid.[25] Just as the other needs in Maslow's hierarchy are irrelevant if physiological needs are not met, an organization cannot operate its cybersecurity management system without effective governance. Policies and procedures may be overlooked, go unenforced, or be under-resourced. Training may be ineffective if it does not carry the weight of the

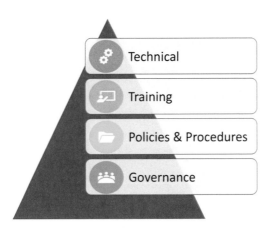

Figure 2-6. Governance is the foundation for effective industrial cybersecurity management.

---

25   Dr. Saul McLeod, "Maslow's Hierarchy of Needs," updated December 29, 2020, accessed June 21, 2021, https://www.simplypsychology.org/maslow.html.

organization's leadership from the top down. Investment in technical controls, without oversight, may be poorly managed with disappointing results.

This hierarchy is especially important in industrial cybersecurity management because the focus is on people and processes. Consider again the example of the gas turbine control system. The priority order of activities for the organization should be as follows:

- Establish the governance that oversees the policies, procedures, training, and technical controls. This governance also presents a visible statement that cybersecurity is a serious matter and controls will be strictly enforced.

- Establish and enforce policies and procedures specific to OT environments (rather than reuse ones appropriate to IT environments) to ensure physical and electronic security is in place, removable media is managed, and operating system updates and antivirus software are properly maintained.

- Train the workforce (including vendors) in the governance, the policies, and the procedures.

- Implement any additional technical controls, such as protocol firewalls between different vendor systems, to minimize the likelihood of compromise through that route.

Chapter 3, "Creating Effective Policy," will address this subject in more detail.

Frameworks, Regulations, Standards, and Guides

There is a great deal of guidance on how to establish a cybersecurity management system, so much that it can be hard to know where to start. Much of the published guidance focuses on IT cybersecurity. As we have seen, there are major differences between the people, process, and technology elements with IT and OT environments. It is essential to adapt the cybersecurity management system to fit within the OT environment, rather than try to change the OT environment to conform to the cybersecurity management system.

The Difference between Frameworks, Regulations, Standards, and Guides

One of the most confusing aspects of guidance is that frameworks, standards, regulations, and guides are often used interchangeably. Each of these serves a different purpose.

- Frameworks provide a high-level overview and guidance to nonexperts but do not provide any guidance on their own. Instead, they refer to standards and guides.

- Regulations are mandatory and enforced by government agencies (e.g., the Department of Energy and the Environmental Protection Agency in the United States, and the Environment Agency and the Office of Rail and Road in the United Kingdom). Failure to comply with regulations can result in fines or even the removal of an organization's license to operate. Regulations usually prescribe what is required, without addressing the process.

- Standards are voluntary documents developed through a formal consensus-driven process that includes rigorous review. Unlike regulations, there is no requirement to use a standard unless it is agreed to in a contract or referred to in a regulation. Courts may use standards in the absence of relevant regulations by applying the "reasonable person" test.

- Guides are also voluntary documents and often confused with standards. The main difference is that guides are produced using a less consensus-driven approach and with less rigor than standards. It takes less time to produce guides, but they are not as universally accepted. Guides are useful introductions to a subject.

The book *Mission Critical Operations Primer*[26] provides more detail on the primary function of regulatory and standards bodies. Although the book focuses on US regulatory and standards bodies, similar organizations in other countries perform the same function.

National Institute of Standards and Technology Cybersecurity Framework

US Presidential Executive Order 13636 ("Improving Critical Infrastructure Cybersecurity") instructed the National Institute of Standards and Technology (NIST) to develop a voluntary cybersecurity framework (CSF) that would provide a "prioritized, flexible, repeatable, performance-based, and cost-effective approach for assisting organizations responsible for critical infrastructure services to manage cybersecurity risk."

In the European Union, The Network and Information Directive (NIS-D), statutory instrument number 360 of 2018, is a legal requirement for operators of essential services (OES). This is based on the NIST CSF.[27]

---

26   Steve Mustard, *Mission Critical Operations Primer* (Research Triangle Park, NC: ISA [International Society of Automation], 2018).

27   "S.I. No. 360/2018 – European Union (Measures for a High Common Level of Security of Network and Information Systems) Regulations 2018," electronic *Irish Statute Book*, accessed June 21, 2021, http://www.irishstatutebook.ie/eli/2018/si/360/made/en.

The definition of *critical infrastructure* in Executive Order 13636 is as follows:

> Systems and assets, whether physical or virtual, so vital to the United States that the incapacity or destruction of such systems and assets would have a debilitating impact on security, national economic security, national public health or safety, or any combination of those matters.

The CSF is structured into five core functions, each of which includes categories and subcategories. This format enables those unfamiliar with the requirements of cybersecurity management to navigate the subject and drill into detail as needed.

The CSF overview is illustrated in Figure 2-7. It shows the five core functions, Identify, Protect, Detect, Respond, and Recover, with their respective categories (e.g., Asset Management, Identity Management, and Access Control).

As noted previously, as a framework, the CSF does not provide any detailed guidance. Instead, the document refers to standards and guides. This format helps readers who are unfamiliar with the standards and guides to navigate the documents.

	Function	Category	ID
What processes and assets need protection?	Identify	Asset Management	ID.AM
		Business Environment	ID.BE
		Governance	ID.GV
		Risk Assessment	ID.RA
		Risk Management Strategy	ID.RM
		Supply Chain Risk Management	ID.SC
What safeguards are available?	Protect	Identity Management & Access Control	PR.AC
		Awareness and Training	PR.AT
		Data Security	PR.DS
		Information Protection Processes & Procedures	PR.IP
		Maintenance	PR.MA
		Protective Technology	PR.PT
What techniques can identify incidents?	Detect	Anomalies and Events	DE.AE
		Security Continuous Monitoring	DE.CM
		Detection Processes	DE.DP
What techniques can contain impacts of incidents?	Respond	Response Planning	RS.RP
		Communications	RS.CO
		Analysis	RS.AN
		Mitigation	RS.MI
		Improvements	RS.IM
What techniques can restore capabilities?	Recover	Recovery Planning	RC.RP
		Improvements	RC.IM
		Communications	RC.CO

Figure 2-7. NIST CSF core functions.[28]

---

28 NIST, "Components of the Cybersecurity Framework," presentation, July 2018, https://www.nist. gov/cyberframework/online-learning/components-framework.

For industrial cybersecurity, the CSF refers to the ISA/IEC 62443 Series of Standards and NIST 800 series guides for its specific guidance. Both of these sources are focused specifically on industrial cybersecurity.

ISA/IEC 62443

The ISA/IEC 62443 Series of Standards addresses the security of industrial automation and control systems (IACSs) throughout their life cycle. These standards and technical reports were initially developed for the industrial process sector but have since been applied to the building automation, medical device, and transportation sectors. Figure 2-8 provides an overview of the family of standards.

There are four tiers in the series of standards. The first two focus on people and processes. The last two focus on technology (systems and components). At the time of writing, some documents are still in development. Key documents in the family include the following:

- **Part 2-1** – Establishing an IACS security program. This helps organizations plan and implement a cybersecurity management system focused on industrial cybersecurity.

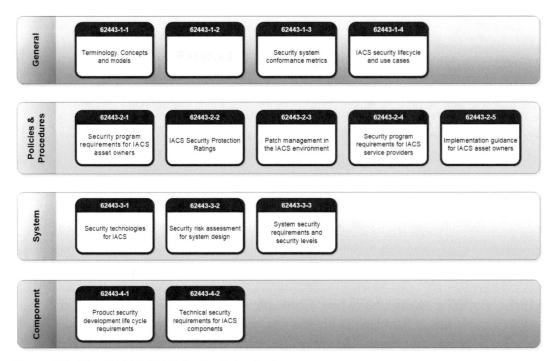

Figure 2-8. The ISA/IEC 62443 family of standards.

- **Part 3-2** – Security risk assessment, system partitioning, and security levels. This describes the requirements for addressing the cybersecurity risks in an IACS, including the use of zones and conduits as well as security levels. These are key aspects of industrial cybersecurity design.

- **Part 3-3** – System security requirements and security levels. This document describes the requirements for an IACS system based on a specified security level. It helps organizations quantify their requirements in universally understood terms.

- **Part 4-1** – Product security development life-cycle requirements. This describes the requirements for a product developer's security development lifecycle.

- **Part 4-2** – Technical security requirements for IACS components. This addresses the requirements for IACS components based on the required security level. Components include devices and applications.

NIST Special Publication 800 Series

The NIST Special Publication 800 series is a series of reports on NIST's information technology laboratory (ITL) research, guidelines, and outreach efforts in information system security. The publication also looks at the ITL's activity with industry, government, and academic organizations. Included in this series is an OT-specific guide, NIST Special Publication 800-82, *Guide to Industrial Control Systems (ICS) Security*. This document provides guidance on how to secure industrial control systems (ICSs), including SCADA systems. It gives direction on securing distributed control systems (DCSs) and other control system configurations, such as PLCs, while addressing their unique performance, reliability, and safety requirements. The document provides an overview of ICS and typical system topologies. It identifies typical threats and vulnerabilities to these systems and provides recommended security countermeasures to mitigate the associated risks.[29]

As noted previously, these documents are guides, not standards. They do not benefit from the consensus and rigor of standards, such as the ISA/IEC 62443 series, and should be used appropriately.

Others

There are many other frameworks, standards, guides, and regulations that relate to cybersecurity. These resources may be required for an organization's industrial

---

29 SP 800-82 Rev. 2, *Guide to Industrial Control Systems (ICS) Security* (Gaithersburg, MD: NIST [National Institute of Standards and Technology], 2015), accessed June 21, 2021, https://csrc.nist.gov/publications/detail/sp/800-82/rev-2/final.

Table 2-2. Additional cybersecurity frameworks, standards, guides, and regulations.

Type	Reference/Title	Use
Regulation	Title 10 CFR – Energy	Nuclear Regulatory Commission (NRC) regulation for the US nuclear industry.
Regulation	Critical Infrastructure Protection (CIP): • CIP-002-5.1a – Cyber Security – BES Cyber System Categorization • CIP-003-6 – Cyber Security – Security Management Controls • CIP-004-6 – Cyber Security – Personnel & Training • CIP-005-5 – Cyber Security – Electronic Security Perimeter(s) • CIP-006-6 – Cyber Security – Physical Security of BES Cyber Systems • CIP-007-6 – Cyber Security – System Security Management • CIP-008-5 – Cyber Security – Incident Reporting and Response Planning • CIP-009-6 – Cyber Security – Recovery Plans for BES Cyber Systems • CIP-010-2 – Cyber Security – Configuration Change Management and Vulnerability Assessments • CIP-011-2 – Cyber Security – Information Protection Related Information • CIP-014-2 – Physical Security	North American Electric Reliability Corporation (NERC) regulation for North American electricity generation and distribution industries.
Regulation	Title 21 CFR Part 11 – Electronic Records; Electronic Signatures – Scope and Application	US Food and Drug Administration (FDA) regulation on businesses producing food, tobacco products, medications, biopharmaceuticals, blood transfusions, medical devices, electromagnetic radiation emitting devices, cosmetics, and animal feed and veterinary products.
Regulation	6 CFR Part 27 – Chemical Facility Anti-Terrorism Standards (CFATS)	US Department of Homeland Security (DHS) regulation for chemical facilities in the United States.
Standard	ISO 61511:2016 – Functional Safety – Safety Instrumented Systems for the Process Industry Sector	International standard that defines practices in the engineering of systems that ensure the safety of an industrial process through the use of instrumentation. It includes an explicit requirement to conduct a security risk assessment (IEC 61511, Part 1, Clause 8.2.4).

Standard	ISO 27001:2013 – Information Technology – Security Techniques – Information Security Management Systems – Requirements	International standard for information security. Although specific to IT systems, there are some overlaps that may need to be considered when developing an industrial cybersecurity management system.
Guide	Center for Internet Security (CIS) Critical Security Controls	Simple guide to the top 20 security controls that should be implemented in IT and OT systems.
Framework	COBIT 5 Control Objectives for Information and Related Technology (ISACA)	Developed by the Information Systems Audit and Control Association (ISACA) to define a set of generic processes for the management of IT.

cybersecurity management system or may need to be understood when developing a system that interacts with an IT cybersecurity management system. Table 2-2 provides some examples. Several are US-specific but typically have equivalents in other countries.

Summary

The aim of this chapter was to differentiate OT and IT cybersecurity and show why these differences are important to an effective cybersecurity management system.

For some time, the difference between OT and IT was explained using the C-I-A triad. C-I-A shows the priority for IT cybersecurity is confidentiality (C), whereas the priority for OT cybersecurity is availability (A). This explanation is too simplistic and requires elaboration to provide a more complete picture.

Within the cybersecurity profession, there is growing appreciation for the consequences of an OT cybersecurity incident. Such incidents may impact the environment, safety, or production. Cybersecurity controls applied to IT need some adaptation before they can be applied to OT—for instance, software patching or network monitoring. However, factors such as the differences in OT and IT projects, and the differences in culture between OT and IT operations, do not receive enough attention. These differences can have significant impacts on OT cybersecurity. There is no single answer to managing OT cybersecurity. The process begins by understanding the differences between IT and OT and then adapting technology, people, and processes in line with those differences.

3

Creating Effective Policy

Introduction

As mentioned in Chapter 2, "What Makes Industrial Cybersecurity Different?," governance is the foundation of a cybersecurity management system. Without effective governance, policies and procedures may be overlooked or go unenforced. Training may be ineffective if it lacks the weight of the organization's leadership, and investment in technical controls may be poorly managed, leading to disappointing results. Despite these clear shortcomings, many organizations implement elements of a cybersecurity management system without good governance in place.

British Standard (BS) 7799, *Information Technology – Code of Practice for Information Security Management*, was first published in 1995. This code formed the basis for the ISO/IEC 27000 family of standards covering information technology (IT) security.

ISO/IEC 27001 states that an information security policy be produced "to provide management direction and support for information security" and an information security infrastructure "to manage information security within the organization."[30]

It should be obvious why governance is paramount and cited at the beginning of this standard. However, this aspect is often overlooked or downplayed, especially in industrial cybersecurity, where additional factors come into play, notably roles and responsibilities.

---

30 ISO/IEC 27001:2013, *Information Technology – Security techniques — Information security management systems — Requirements* (Geneva 20 – Switzerland: IEC [International Electrotechnical Commission] and ISO [International Organization for Standardization]).

The common mistakes in industrial cybersecurity governance stem from a failure to complete one or more of the following tasks:

- Establish the governance infrastructure.

- Assign senior management representation.

- Allocate resources and assign clear ownership.

- Establish good oversight.

- Communicate to the organization.

Establish the Governance Infrastructure

The key elements of a good governance infrastructure are as follows:

- A committee of stakeholders representing all parts of the organization.

- A clear, written charter defining the terms of reference of the committee. This document should be signed by all members and openly shared with the wider organization.

- Regular reporting to the committee, which includes key performance indicators (KPIs) representing the cybersecurity posture of the organization. This must distinguish between the IT and operational technology (OT) elements of the organization.

- Regular meetings at a frequency sufficient to enable reports to be analyzed and actions authorized.

The committee charter defines all these elements. It should be no more than two pages in length; if it is any longer, it will contain too many details to manage and enforce. The charter should be issued by senior leadership and clearly and concisely state:

- The committee's purpose

- The committee's composition

- The committee's responsibilities and duties

- The meeting arrangements

- The reporting arrangements

The composition of an industrial cybersecurity governance committee will vary from organization to organization. In some cases, the committee will include the director of each department. In others, it may be composed of a small number of leaders drawn from the board of directors.

Figure 3-1 shows an example of a cybersecurity committee charter.

Assign Senior Management Representation

"Boards that choose to ignore, or minimize, the importance of cybersecurity responsibility do so at their own peril."

Luis A. Aguilar, Commissioner of the US Securities and Exchange Commission[31]

Although the composition of an industrial cybersecurity governance committee will vary from organization to organization, it must

- report directly to the board of directors, and

- include decision makers who oversee all resources of the organization.

If the governance committee does not report directly to the board of directors, this indicates that the board of directors is either not fully aware of the organization's cybersecurity risks or is not correctly assessing the risks. Surveys and industry reviews now consistently show cybersecurity to be a top 10 risk for organizations.[32]

Allocate Resources and Assign Clear Ownership

Even with a clear charter, managing cybersecurity can be a challenge if ownership and responsibility are unclear. This is especially true with industrial cybersecurity. Most organizations with industrial control and automation systems organize IT and OT into separate groups. OT is a relatively new term created to help identify the technology used in the production or manufacturing end of a business. While most organizations have an IT department, very few have an OT department. The group responsible for OT is typically called *engineering* or *operations*. Traditionally, there has been a clear demarcation between IT and OT, at least when viewed from the Purdue model perspective, such as in Figure 3-2.

---

31 Luis A. Aguilar, "Boards of Directors, Corporate Governance, and Cyber-Risks, Sharpening the Focus," speech June 10, 2014, at the "Cyber Risks and the Boardroom" Conference in New York, NY, https://www.sec.gov/news/speech/2014-spch061014laa.
32 Such as the 2019 survey by North Carolina State University's enterprise risk management (ERM) initiative and global consulting firm Protiviti shown in Table 3-1.

CYBERSECURITY COMMITTEE CHARTER

PURPOSE

The Cybersecurity Committee is an advisory and oversight committee of the Board of Directors of the Company. The Committee's purpose shall include, but not be limited to:

- Assisting with the Board of Directors' understanding and oversight of:
  - the Company's compliance with its cybersecurity requirements, policies, controls, and procedures
  - the identification and management of cybersecurity risks
  - the preparation and planning for potential cybersecurity incidents
- Maintaining, through regularly scheduled meetings, a line of communication between the Board of Directors and the Company's management as it pertains to cybersecurity.

COMPOSITION AND QUALIFICATIONS

The Audit Committee shall be comprised of three or more Directors appointed by the Board of Directors. The Board of Directors shall designate one of the members of the Committee as its chairperson.

RESPONSIBILITIES AND DUTIES

The Committee's responsibilities and duties include, but are not limited to:

1. Review changes to standards, policies, or procedures that relate to cybersecurity.

2. Review and discuss any non-conformances, or problems, or difficulties in achieving conformance with the Company's standards, policies, or procedures.

3. Oversee the structure, operation, and efficacy of any programs relating to cybersecurity.

4. Review reports from management regarding, among other things, cybersecurity incidents and employee cybersecurity training, awareness, and evaluation programs.

5. Have authority to form a sub-committee of the Committee.

6. Have such other duties as may be delegated from time to time by the Board of Directors.

7. Make such recommendations to the Board of Directors with respect to any of the above and other matters relating to cybersecurity.

MEETINGS

The Committee shall meet at least quarterly or more frequently if circumstances dictate. A majority of the members then serving on the Committee shall constitute a quorum.

OUTSIDE ADVISERS

The Committee, in its sole discretion, shall have the authority to retain or obtain the advice of one or more consultants, or other advisers. The Committee shall be directly responsible for the appointment, compensation, retention, and oversight of the work of any such advisers retained by the Committee. In addition, PCT shall provide appropriate funding, as determined by the Committee, for the payment of reasonable compensation to such consultants and other advisers retained by the Committee.

-1-

Figure 3-1. Example of a cybersecurity committee charter.

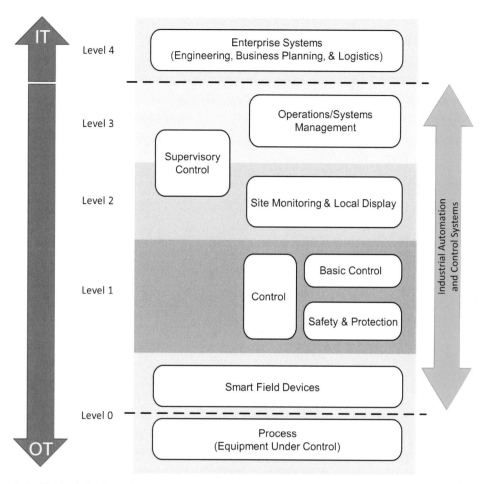

Figure 3-2. Typical division of responsibilities between IT and OT.

In simple terms, IT is responsible for the systems and networks in the office environment (known colloquially as "the carpeted area"). OT is responsible for the systems and networks in the production or manufacturing environment ("the noncarpeted area"). The physical division between the two is referred to as the *demilitarized zone* (DMZ). The DMZ represents an interface between the two environments, designed to secure communications between them.

In practical terms, the division of responsibilities is often complicated. Organizations may have their IT department responsible for operating system updates and antivirus management of all servers and workstations. That would include those in the OT environment. Some organizations may have the OT team take responsibility for these activities but have IT provide oversight and report on nonconformances. Regardless, it is essential that these responsibilities are documented and clearly understood by all parties. The organization must have the flexibility to adjust and optimize the division of responsibilities. This might mean changing team structures to support a multidisciplinary approach. This adaptation may not fit within the conventional organization structure, but it may be the best option from a cybersecurity management perspective. One of the biggest challenges in creating a multidisciplinary team is convincing each group that they need the other. The IT specialists do not have the detailed system understanding that OT specialists have. IT specialists do provide critical elements of a well-defined cybersecurity management system, but this must be executed correctly.

The often-used responsibility assignment matrix (RACI) illustrates a responsibility hierarchy. The RACI acronym stands for responsible, accountable, consulted, and informed. The common pitfalls of a RACI chart/matrix are as follows:

- RACI terms are poorly defined.

- The matrix is created in isolation without input from all stakeholders.

- It is time-consuming to create.

- It is often ignored once approved.

The most commonly misunderstood RACI terms are *responsible* and *accountable*. *Accountable* means ultimately responsible for the task, whereas *responsible* refers to accomplishing the task. More than one person may be responsible for an activity, but only one person is accountable for any activity.

The confusion extends to *consulted* and *informed*. Being *consulted* means providing feedback that may be incorporated in the decision. Being *informed* does not include the feedback option. As a result, it is common for the consulted role to be overused. To avoid confusion, other models have been developed using different terms:

- **RAS:** Responsible, approve, support

- **DACI:** Driver, approver, consulted, informed

- **CLAM:** Contributes, leads, approves, monitors

Using RACI or any one of these options should be at the organization's discretion. The objective is to clearly define and agree on who does the work and who is responsible for what is done. A simple example using CLAM terminology is shown in Figure 3-3.

In many operational facilities, tasks are performed by vendors or service providers. It is even more important to accurately capture responsibilities in these scenarios. Many

	Engineering Operations	Engineering Director	IT Operations	IT Director	Chief Information Security Officer
Server Backups	C	M	L	M	M
Workstation Backups	C	M	L	M	M
Programmable Logic Controller (PLC) Backups	L	M	C	M	M
Server Updates	L	M	C	M	M
Workstation Updates	L	M	C	M	M
PLC Updates	L	M	C	M	M
Antivirus Updates	L	M	C	M	M
Network Monitoring	C	M	L	M	M
Security incident response	C	C	C	C	L

Figure 3-3. Simple responsibility assignment matrix example.

organizations rely on unwritten agreements or practices that can be easily misinterpreted. In one anecdote from a critical sector operator, a third party was assigned the task of performing backups. It was only by chance that the operator discovered that this task was not being performed. The operator has changed the provider and now includes oversight as part of its processes.

If the responsibility assignment matrix produced appears to be overly complex or long, or it is hard to identify the roles, it may be that the organization's structure is not optimized for cybersecurity management. This is a useful outcome. It identifies areas where an organization might restructure or streamline teams.

Too often, responsibility assignment matrices end up filed away and never used. The matrix may look good on paper but does not properly address the organization's policies and procedures. In most organizations, industrial cybersecurity duties are added to existing roles. These additional duties can easily be neglected in favor of well-established activities. It is also common to underestimate the effort required to perform industrial cybersecurity duties. At the very least, it is unreasonable to place additional duties on employees without ensuring they have the capacity to undertake them. Doing so without oversight creates additional cybersecurity vulnerabilities as tasks are skipped. In the European Union, this failure to provide sufficient resources is a legal issue. The Network and Information Systems (NIS) directive

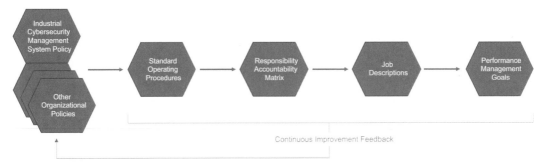

Figure 3-4. The importance of integrating responsibilities and accountabilities.

places legal obligations on all providers of critical infrastructure (operators of essential services—OES) to ensure they are prepared to deal with the increasing volume of cyber threats.[33]

For these reasons, it is essential to create a clear relationship between policies, standard operating procedures, the responsibility assignment matrix, and formal job descriptions. Such a relationship is shown in Figure 3-4. This facilitates a clear understanding of expectations and ensures all activities are correctly managed.

Continuous improvement is an essential part of any organization. Situations change, meaning initial ideas on responsibility and accountability may no longer match reality. The continuous improvement process should identify performance goals, based on job descriptions, and review these goals regularly. Honest feedback on what works and what does not will improve organizational performance and efficiency.

Establish Good Oversight

The governance board needs accurate, reliable, and timely information to be effective. This includes:

- **Reporting cybersecurity management system effectiveness** – How well is the existing cybersecurity management system working? Are there areas that must be improved to comply with current expectations?

---

33 Information Commissioner's Office, "The Guide to NIS," accessed June 21, 2021, https://ico.org.uk/for-organisations/the-guide-to-nis.

- **Tracking and managing cybersecurity risk** – What risks does the organization face? Are these risks being managed to a level that is "as low as reasonably practicable"?[34]

- **Monitoring changes** – What new cybersecurity threats are on the rise, and how will they affect the organization? Does the cybersecurity management system need to be adjusted?

Many industrial cybersecurity management programs ultimately fail because of poor oversight. Many more become ineffective or inefficient because the organization fails to continuously improve the program.

The paradox of cybersecurity is that the absence of an incident with visible consequences can be attributed to a successful management program. However, many major incidents go unnoticed or unreported, and some operators can have advanced persistent threats (APTs) lurking in their system, exfiltrating sensitive information, analyzing vulnerabilities, or collecting data to prepare for a future cyberattack. The December 23, 2015, cyberattack on the Ukrainian regional electricity distribution companies Kyivoblenergo, Prykarpattyaoblenergo, and Chernivtsioblenergo, which left 230,000 customers without power for several hours, began with a spear-phishing campaign in the spring of 2015. The attackers were able to probe around networks unnoticed for many months before the attack.[35]

Reporting Cybersecurity Management System Effectiveness

There is no definitive list of cybersecurity KPIs. They must be chosen by the organization to support the oversight, as noted earlier.

When choosing KPIs, consider whether the indicator is lagging or leading. Lagging indicators are easy to measure but hard to improve. Leading indicators are hard to measure but easier to influence. In addition, lagging indicators tend to relate to overall

---

34 This term, abbreviated as ALARP, has its origins in health and safety legislation (originally from the UK Health and Safety at Work Act of 1974) and means that a risk must be mitigated unless the cost of doing so would reasonably be seen as excessive. For example, the risk of using universal serial bus (USB) ports on a personal computer can be mitigated easily and cheaply by the use of firmware disabling or USB locks, but with residual risk (that the ports could be reenabled or unlocked). Building a custom workstation with the USB ports physically removed would result in no residual risk but would be disproportionately expensive. In most applications, the use of firmware disabling USB ports or USB locks would be seen as reducing the risk to as low as reasonably practicable.

35 Amy Krigman, "Cyber Autopsy Series: Ukrainian Power Grid Attack Makes History," GlobalSign Blog, October 22, 2020, accessed June 21, 2021, https://www.globalsign.com/en/blog/cyber-autopsy-series-ukranian-power-grid-attack-makes-history.

organization performance. Leading indicators are often related to activities under-taken by individuals. This is another reason leading indicators are easier to influence.

A simple example is weight loss. Weight is a lagging indicator and easy to measure. Two useful leading indicators of weight are calorific input (e.g., food intake) and calo-rific output (exercise). Calorific input and output are harder to measure than weight (e.g., calorific output depends on body weight, as well as time and type of exercise) but easy to manage (i.e., you can choose how much you eat or how much exercise you do).

In health and safety management, lagging and leading indicators are critically impor-tant. Figure 3-5 shows the relationship between leading and lagging indicators for health and safety in the form of the accident triangle, also known as *Heinrich's triangle* or *Bird's triangle*. The accident triangle is widely used in industries with health and safety risks. It is often adapted to include regional or organization-specific terms (e.g., *HiPo* or *High Potential Accident* instead of *Serious Accidents*) or to provide further catego-rization (e.g., showing Days Away from Work Cases and Recordable Injuries as types of Minor Accidents).

The accident triangle clearly shows the relationship between the earlier, more minor incidents and the later, more serious ones. This relationship can also be expressed in terms of leading and lagging indicators. In the accident triangle in Figure 3-5, unsafe

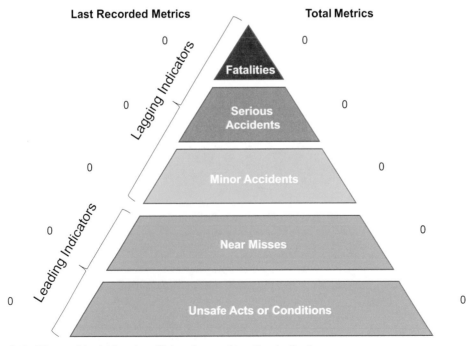

Figure 3-5. The accident triangle with lagging and leading indicators.

acts or conditions and near misses are leading indicators of health and safety issues. As these numbers increase, so does the likelihood of more serious incidents. These more serious incidents are the lagging indicators. To minimize serious health and safety incidents, organizations monitor leading indicators such as unsafe acts or near misses.

Monitoring near misses through safety observations (and encouraging employees to report them), coupled with regular audits to check that employees are following their training and procedures, creates leading indicators that can be adjusted. For example, employees can be prompted to complete assigned safety training. Observations and audits will show if this training must be adjusted. The goal is to improve safety as reflected in lagging indicators.

If there is a mismatch between leading and lagging indicators (e.g., leading indicators are within expectations but lagging indicators are still poor), the organization can review them to identify additional leading indicators.

Most cybersecurity metrics used today are lagging indicators. They are outcomes, such as the number of cybersecurity incidents experienced, or the time to detect, identify, contain, or resolve an incident. To manage cybersecurity, an organization must identify leading indicators that influence the lagging indicators. A sample security triangle, based on the safety triangle, is shown in Figure 3-6.

This security triangle highlights the major problem with cybersecurity monitoring and reporting: Tracking only minor, HiPo (high potential), and major security incidents

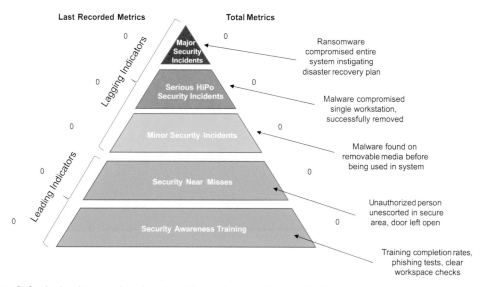

Figure 3-6. A simple security triangle with lagging and leading indicators.

(the lagging indicators) will give a false sense of confidence about a cybersecurity management program. Poor performance on leading indicators is a better predictor of security risk. Tracking these indicators gives the organization an opportunity to make adjustments that will reduce cybersecurity risk. The security triangle should highlight the importance of security awareness training and encourage reporting of security near misses.

To obtain sufficient leading indicators, it may be necessary to deploy additional monitoring tools. For example, monitoring the status of antivirus software on machines could yield additional data on security near misses that might otherwise go unnoticed.

Tracking and Managing Cybersecurity Risk

Table 3-1 shows the results of a 2019 survey by North Carolina State University's enterprise risk management (ERM) initiative and global consulting firm Protiviti. It involved 1,063 respondents from boards of directors and C-suite functions. The figure shows their risk priorities for 2020.[36] In this survey, cybersecurity is ranked twice in the top 10: Risk

Table 3-1. Top 10 risks for 2020.

	Risk Issue	2020*	2019 (rank*)
1	Impact of regulatory change and scrutiny on operational resilience, products, and services	6.38	6.24 (3)
2	Economic conditions impacting growth	6.34	5.93 (11)
3	Succession challenges; ability to attract and retain top talent	6.27	6.34 (2)
4	Ability to compete with "born digital" and other competitors	6.23	6.35 (1)
5	Resistance to change operations	6.15	6.17 (5)
6	Cyber threats	6.09	6.18 (4)
7	Privacy/identity management and information security	6.06	6.13 (7)
8	Organization's culture may not sufficiently encourage timely identification and escalation of risk issues	5.83	5.99 (9)
9	Sustaining customer loyalty and retention	5.82	5.95 (10)
10	Adoption of digital technologies may require new skills or significant efforts to upskill/reskill existing employees (new in 2020)	5.71	N/A (new)

Scores are based on a 10-point scale, with "10" representing that the risk issue will have an extensive impact on the organization.

---

[36] North Carolina State University and Protiviti, "Illuminating the Top Global Risks in 2020," accessed June 21, 2021, https://www.protiviti.com/US-en/2020-top-risks.

6 (cyber threats) and Risk 7 (privacy/identity management and information security). In addition, cybersecurity affects or is affected by all the other risks in this top 10:

- Risk 1, *impact of regulatory change and scrutiny on operational resilience, products, and services*: Loss of operational resilience is a major consequence of a cyber incident, especially in industrial cybersecurity when loss of system availability can result in loss of production.

- Risk 2, *economic conditions impacting growth*; Risk 4, *ability to compete with "born digital" and other competitors*; and Risk 9, *sustaining customer loyalty and retention*: All necessitate the introduction of new technology that, in turn, affects the cyber posture.

- Risk 3, *succession challenges, ability to attract and retain top talent*; and Risk 10, *adoption of digital technologies may require new skills or significant efforts to upskill/reskill existing employees*: Skills and knowledge in cybersecurity, particularly industrial cybersecurity, continue to be in short supply. In addition, technology, and the associated cybersecurity vulnerabilities, continue to change.

- Risk 5, *resistance to change operations*; and Risk 8, *organization's culture may not sufficiently encourage timely identification and escalation of risk issues*: In most organizations, the resistance to change is a major cause in the failure to operate a good cybersecurity management system. One significant factor is the lack of clarity in ownership. As a result, risks are not identified, escalated, or owned. This will be discussed next.

While this survey is encouraging, it indicates that, for most organizations, the focus will be on information security and privacy issues. Industrial cybersecurity is still not well understood by boards, although production availability, safety, and environmental harm are. Chapter 4, "Measure to Manage Cybersecurity Risk," will discuss methods to leverage this awareness when presenting cybersecurity risk to senior management.

Even if the governance committee reports to the board of directors, it must be empowered to make key decisions with respect to cybersecurity controls. Otherwise, reporting and meetings will become perfunctory or not happen at all.

Often an organization will make a significant investment to establish an industrial cybersecurity management system but then fail in the governance. This could mean failing to appoint the right individuals or failing to establish an effective charter. As a result, the progress made during this establishment phase either ceases entirely or, in some cases, the organization lapses back to its prior posture.

Monitoring Changes

A key role for the governance board is to monitor the changing circumstances that impact the organization's risk and, potentially, the cybersecurity management system.

- **Review and approval of operational support decisions relating to industrial cybersecurity** – Often decisions made at the operational level have a major impact on an organization's cybersecurity preparedness (e.g., the decision whether to purchase spare parts, such as workstations, PLC cards, and network devices).

- **Review of changes to risk assessment** – The cybersecurity risk assessment is subject to constant change. This is in response to external threats, new vulnerabilities, and organizational changes.

- **Review of changes to the cybersecurity management system** – In addition to organizational changes resulting from operational support decisions or risk assessments, it may be necessary to make changes to the cybersecurity management system. For example, audits may highlight gaps that must be closed, incident investigations may identify improvements, or benchmarking may identify new best practices.

These considerations will be reviewed in more detail later in this book. For now, it is enough to highlight that decision-making at the governance board level leads to greater consistency across the organization and helps manage everyone's expectations. These three change monitoring items should be included in a standing agenda for the governance board.

A warning regarding record keeping: In the age of email, instant messaging, and collaborative tools, it has become normal to bypass good documentation practices and make decisions more informally. Good documentation practices are essential to effective industrial cybersecurity management. Documentation need not be onerous, but for any decisions, a short document should be presented to the governance board. The board should signify their approval on the final version. This document is then retained centrally for ease of access. This approach allows decisions to be re-reviewed as necessary and ensures proper procedures are not bypassed.

Communicate to the Organization

The work to establish good governance can be undermined if it is not communicated throughout the organization. The governance board should make available to the organization:

- The governance charter

- The supporting policies and procedures

- The responsibility assignment matrix

- Regular reports on lagging and leading indicators

- Prompt reports on cybersecurity incidents

- Compliance and benchmarking results

All information should be shared within the organization and with any relevant external parties, such as the Department of Homeland Security in the United States and the National Cyber Security Centre (NCSC) in the United Kingdom. Sharing the information, good or bad, helps to make all employees feel they are part of the results. Sharing with relevant external parties helps build a clearer picture of the situation that all critical infrastructure operators face. Reports should be issued regularly (in line with health and safety reporting) to reinforce that the organization takes its cybersecurity responsibilities seriously.

Common mistakes organizations make with information sharing are shown in Table 3-2.

Regular Reports on Lagging and Leading Indicators

The security triangle shown in Figure 3-6 provided a simple set of leading and lagging indicators.

The lagging indicators suggested are suitable for most organizations:

- Minor security incidents

- High-potential security incidents

- Major security incidents

However, an organization may choose to monitor a wider range of leading indicators, including the following:

- Status of asset inventory

- Number of intrusion attempts

- Number of cybersecurity near misses

Table 3-2. Common mistakes in cybersecurity information sharing.

Mistake	Result	Correct Approach
Sharing only positive reports or messages or downplaying bad news to senior management	1. Funding is cut because it appears to not be needed. 2. There is significant surprise and disappointment when an incident occurs.	Share information openly and honestly.
Overselling value of technical controls to the organization	1. There is a perception that everything is under control, therefore personnel do not need to be vigilant.	Ensure everyone is aware that people and process are always the weakest links, regardless of technical controls.
Declaring the details of cybersecurity incidents to be classified, and thus limiting the sharing of these incidents within the organization	1. Lessons are not learned by those who are most likely to be involved in similar incidents. 2. Lack of incident reporting creates a sense that cybersecurity is not a major problem.	Censor and redact details as necessary but ensure that all incidents, including near misses, are promptly reported. Reporting improves awareness and encourages improvement, and prompt reporting inspires a sense of urgency in addressing issues.
IT departments acting independently of OT departments when engaging on cybersecurity	1. Incomplete view of cybersecurity risk in the organization or with regulators and other authorities. 2. Lack of investment as a result of incomplete view of risk.	OT department defines and manages risk and IT department supports OT department with services to help manage that risk.

- Time to apply approved patches

- Number of systems with known vulnerabilities

- Time between backup restoration tests

- Number of users with *super user* access level

- Number of days to deactivate former employee credentials

- Frequency of third-party access by each third party

- Frequency of business continuity or disaster recovery test(s)

- Percentage of business partners with effective cybersecurity policies

Collecting the data to track these indicators can involve significant cost and effort. In some cases, an organization may lack access to the data needed. There is also an infrastructure requirement to achieve this data collection. Once the data is collectible, it must be analyzed and presented in a suitable format. Cybersecurity vendors offer solutions, including reporting dashboards. Organizations can develop their own

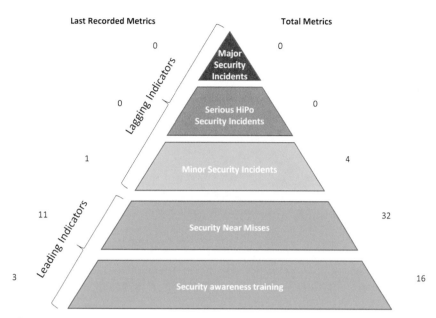

Figure 3-7. Security triangle showing real data.

in-house reporting solutions if they have such a capability. The key with cybersecurity metrics and reporting, like any other type of reporting, is to:

- Focus on the measures that are meaningful to the organization. Just because it is possible to measure does not necessarily mean the measurement is useful.

- Focus on the relationship between leading and lagging indicators. The security triangle is an essential visual.

Like the safety triangle, the security triangle, as shown in Figure 3-7, clearly shows the relationship between the leading and lagging indicators. The focus must be on managing the leading indicators. A more detailed security dashboard will be required to generate the data in the security triangle, but the security triangle provides a snapshot of cybersecurity performance.

Prompt Reporting of Cybersecurity Incidents

There are two aspects to prompt reporting:

1. Providing the means for and encouraging employees to report cybersecurity observations or near misses as they happen

2. Reporting cybersecurity incidents to employees together with any lessons learned and guidance

Training, empowerment, and development of a cyberculture are key. Again, it is helpful to leverage practices from the health and safety community for both cases.

Reporting Cybersecurity Observations or Near Misses

Figure 3-8 shows a simple safety observation card that is available from OSHA. Such cards are usually provided around a facility to enable anyone to document an observation as it happens. The form is designed to require minimal effort and encourage completion. After an observation card is completed, it is usually posted to a recognized receptacle in the facility or handed to a supervisor. Observations are collated, reviewed, and discussed at daily safety briefings.

LOGO HERE		LOGO HERE	
QUICK SAFETY OBSERVATION CARD		**QUICK SAFETY OBSERVATION CARD**	
Observation Title:		**Corrective Actions**	
		Hierarchy of Controls (circle one):	
		NA	
Date Observed: / /	Observer:	Elimination / Substitution / Engineering / Admin / PPE	
		Corrective Action Title:	
Physical Location of Observation (Dept / Area):		1 - Corrective Action Details:	
Circle One:			
Safe Behavior / Unsafe Behavior / Unsafe Condition		Corrective Action Assigned To:	Due Date: / /
Description:		2 - Corrective Action Details:	
Immediate Action Taken:		Corrective Action Assigned To:	Due Date: / /

Figure 3-8. A simple safety observation card (front and back).

Source: Reproduced from OSHA.[37]

37 Occupational Health and Safety Hub, Quick Safety Observation Card – Free Template, https://ohshub.com/quick-safety-observation-card-free-template/.

A key aspect of safety observations is reporting any unsafe behavior, no matter how minor it may appear. In general, employees are empowered to stop any work if they believe it is unsafe. This includes overriding seniority. This approach ensures the safety of everyone in a critical infrastructure facility.

The example in Figure 3-8 allows anyone to report positive safety behavior. This provides positive reinforcement to employees while raising safety awareness.

For cybersecurity observations, the safety observation card in Figure 3-9 could be modified as follows:

- Replace "Safe Behavior/Unsafe Behavior/Unsafe Condition" with "Secure Behavior/Insecure Behavior/Insecure Condition."

- Replace the list under "Hierarchy of Controls" with cybersecurity controls employed in the organization, for example, "Antivirus Protection/Operating System Patching/Access Control/Backup and Recovery/Removable Media."

The resulting cybersecurity observations should be collated, reviewed, and discussed at daily safety briefings alongside the safety observations. This elevates the importance of the cybersecurity observations in the minds of the employees.

Reporting Cybersecurity Incidents to Employees

Lessons-learned reports are routinely published in most industrial organizations. The goal is to learn from mistakes and improve health and safety. The reports differ among organizations, but generally include the following:

- A description of the incident

- The results of the investigation (e.g., why the incident happened)

- Guidance to avoid reoccurrences of the incident (the solution and the reminders or learnings)

Such reports are issued quickly upon conclusion of incident investigations. This minimizes the chance of reoccurrence.

There is reluctance to produce similar reports for cybersecurity incidents, even within an organization, the assumption being that even company-restricted information can find its way outside the organization.

Table 3-3. Common concerns over cybersecurity reporting.

Concern	Counterargument
Publicizing vulnerabilities exploited in the incident	Other than a rare occurrence concerning a zero-day vulnerability,[38] most vulnerabilities are already well publicized. A failure to address well-known vulnerabilities is a separate problem that the organization must address more urgently.
Publicizing new controls designed to avoid future incidents	Like vulnerabilities, cybersecurity controls are well understood, and it is unlikely that an organization has a proprietary control that it cannot risk being disclosed.
Regulatory punishments	Regulatory reporting cannot and should not be circumvented.
Public disclosure could harm reputation	The impact on reputation is much greater if disclosure is withheld.

Assuming the organization is aware that an incident has occurred, the most common reasons the author has heard for withholding reporting are listed in Table 3-3 with counterarguments.

The arguments in Table 3-3 could apply to health and safety incidents. However, the advent of "safety culture" has demonstrated that the benefits of open reporting are greater than any potential downside.

Failing to report cybersecurity incidents leads to the misconception that cybersecurity is not a major problem. If nobody in the organization hears about real incidents, they may let their guard down, dismissing the warnings and guidance.

Monitoring Compliance and Benchmarking

Over time, an organization that does not experience major incidents may convince itself, in isolation, that its policies and procedures are sound, only to learn otherwise when an attack occurs. To guard against such complacency requires the creation of benchmarks based on external industry standards and guidance.

Monitoring Against Policy

A cybersecurity policy is not something that is written and filed away. The purpose of a cybersecurity policy is to define the necessary activities and behaviors to manage the associated risks. Therefore, this policy should be at the forefront of the governance process. It provides a yardstick for the organization's performance.

---

38 A zero-day (also known as *0-day*) vulnerability is one that is unknown to or unaddressed by the product vendor or the user. Until the vulnerability is mitigated, it can be exploited to adversely affect operation.

Cybersecurity Compliance

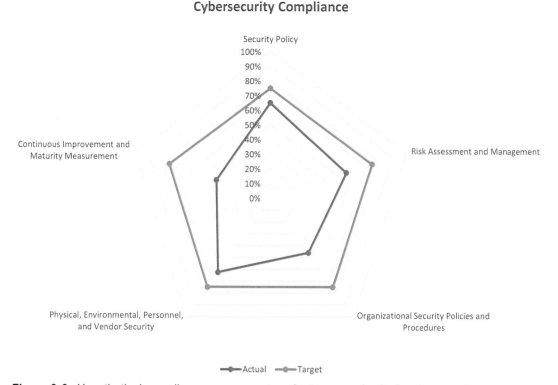

Figure 3-9. Hypothetical compliance assessment against an organization's cybersecurity policy.

Every organization is different. Cybersecurity policies should reflect these differences, but all will contain several key sections. Figure 3-9 shows a hypothetical example of a compliance assessment against a cybersecurity policy that has the following sections:

- Security Policy

- Risk Assessment and Management

- Organizational Security Policies and Procedures

- Physical, Environmental, Personnel, and Vendor Security

- Continuous Improvement and Maturity Management

The *radar chart* shows how the organization is performing against the policy, comparing the percentage of compliance for each section against a target.

The target for each section will be determined by the governance body. It may be based on comparison with other organizations or other data.

Table 3-4. Calculating compliance.

Numbered Reference	Clause Text	Response	Weight	Max score	Actual score	% Compliance
1.2.3.1	Policy requirement #1 detail	P	H	6	3	50%
1.2.3.2	Policy requirement #2 detail	N	M	4	0	0%
1.2.3.3	Policy requirement #3 detail	F	L	2	2	100%
1.2.3.4	Policy requirement #4 detail	N	H	6	0	0%
	Overall result			18	5	27.8%

To determine the percentage of compliance, the organization tracks whether it is meeting the individual requirements of the section. Table 3-4 shows a simplified example of a section with four requirements. For each requirement, the response options are:

- F – Fully compliant

- P – Partially compliant

- N – Noncompliant

Each requirement is given a weight. This weighting represents the importance of the requirement to the organization. In this case, the weighting is either H(igh), M(edium), or L(ow). The weighting determines the maximum score for the requirement; in this example, H = 6, M = 4, and L = 2.

To determine the actual score for each requirement, the maximum score and response are combined, such that a fully compliant response (F) results in 100% of the maximum score. Partially compliant (P) results in 50% of the maximum score. Noncompliant (N) results in 0% of the maximum score. The overall maximum and actual scores are used to determine the overall percentage of compliance for the section. This is one of many ways to calculate compliance.

This result is plotted against the target compliance for the section on the radar chart shown in Figure 3-9.

Monitoring Against Industry Standards

It is not enough for an organization to monitor its performance against its own policy. Without reference to external measures, there is no way of knowing how good this performance really is. Unfortunately, many organizations track their own performance with little or no reference to external measures. They become convinced they are doing well, when in reality they may be at risk.

Many external measures are available for an organization to use. The ISA/IEC 62443 series contains the only international cybersecurity standards for industrial control and automation systems. There are also guides from the National Institute of Standards and Technology (NIST) (the 800 series), as well as regulations from government bodies such as North American Electric Reliability Corporation Critical Infrastructure Protection (NERC CIP) and Cybersecurity and Infrastructure Security Agency Chemical Facility Anti-Terrorism Standard (CISA CFATS).

The NIST Cybersecurity Framework (CSF) is not a standard, but it is an internationally recognized guide for managing cybersecurity. The NIST CSF has five core functions: Identify, Protect, Detect, Respond, and Recover. It also includes a list of requirements for each function, referring to the standards, guides, and regulations mentioned earlier.

Figure 3-10 shows a hypothetical organization's compliance against the five core functions of the NIST NSF. This can be calculated in a similar manner to the organization's own policy, described previously.

Tracking compliance will help an organization understand where it is with regard to the overall industry.

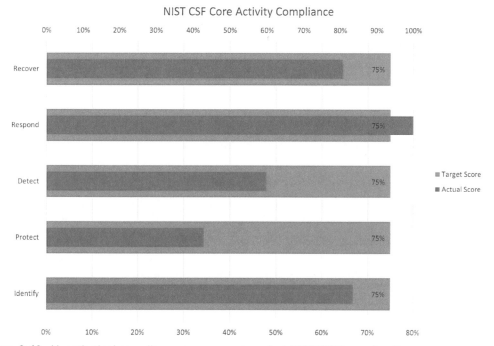

Figure 3-10. Hypothetical compliance assessment against NIST CSF core functions.

Table 3-5. SANS cybersecurity maturity model level definitions.

Level 1 No Security Awareness Program	No attempt is made to train and educate the organization. People do not know or understand organizational policies and procedures, do not realize they are a target, and are highly vulnerable to most human-based attacks.
Level 2 Compliance Focused	Awareness program is designed primarily to meet specific compliance or audit requirements. Training is limited to annual or ad hoc basis, such as an on-site presentation once a year or quarterly newsletters. There is no attempt to change behavior. Employees are unsure of organizational policies, their role in protecting their organization's information assets, and how to prevent, identify, or report a security incident.
Level 3 Promoting Awareness and Change	Awareness program identifies the training topics that have the greatest impact on supporting the organization's mission and focuses on those key topics. Program goes beyond annual training and includes continual reinforcement throughout the year. Content is communicated in an engaging and positive manner that encourages behavior change at work, at home, and while traveling. As a result, employees are aware of policies/processes and actively prevent, recognize, and report incidents.
Level 4 Long-Term Sustainment	Long-term sustainment builds on an existing program that is promoting awareness and change, adding the processes and resources for a long-term life cycle, including at a minimum an annual review, and updating both training content and communication methods. As a result, the program becomes an established part of the organization's culture and is always current and engaging.
Level 5 Metrics	Defined as a security awareness program that has metrics in place to track progress and measure impact. As a result, the program is continuously improving and able to demonstrate a return on investment.

Lance Spitzner of SANS produced a *cybersecurity awareness maturity model* that helps organizations understand how well developed their program is and how far they may still have to go. This is described in Table 3-5.[39]

Summary

The most common failure in industrial cybersecurity governance arises from a failure to properly execute one or more of the following tasks:

- Establish the governance infrastructure

- Assign senior management representation

- Allocate resources and assign clear ownership

- Establish good oversight

- Communicate to the organization

---

39 Lance Spitzner, "Security Awareness Maturity Model," January 1, 2019, accessed June 21, 2021, https://www.sans.org/security-awareness-training/blog/security-awareness-maturity-model/.

Without supporting infrastructure or senior management engagement, an industrial cybersecurity program will eventually dissipate. The organization will slip back into business as usual, reacting again only after periodic audits flag noncompliance.

With clear ownership and good oversight, it is possible to maintain a focus on cybersecurity, along with other business-critical areas such as safety. In fact, the cybersecurity community can learn a lot from their safety management colleagues. Safety culture is embedded in organizations. As a result, it is at the forefront of everyone's mind. Another aspect of good safety management is communication. The more organization leaders and staff hear about cybersecurity, especially near misses and other performance metrics, the more likely they are to internalize the issue and take it seriously.

4 | Measure to Manage Risk

Introduction

There are many books on the subject of risk management. This chapter is not intended to cover the basic principles described in those books. Instead, the aim is to explain how industrial cybersecurity risks are different, and how those risks can be quantified and managed. This chapter will look beyond how industrial cybersecurity risks are currently managed to propose more effective approaches.

One common theme in cybersecurity is a reluctance to use probability and statistics when estimating the likelihood of an incident. This chapter will provide guidance on how probability and statistics can be applied to deliver more useful results.

The recommended reading list provides several resources that describe the basics of risk management in more detail. These resources offer more insight into how probability and statistics can be used in cybersecurity.

A Brief Overview of Risk Management

The Importance of Risk Management

Risk is "the effect of uncertainty on objectives," and risk management is the "coordinated set of activities and methods that is used to direct an organization and to control the many risks that can affect its ability to achieve objectives."

A common theme throughout this book is that the industrial cybersecurity community should learn from the safety community. This is especially true when it comes to risk management.

After the Piper Alpha disaster of 1988 (see Figure 4-1), in which 167 people were killed in a series of explosions and fires that destroyed a production platform, major changes were made to the safety and risk management in the oil and gas industry. These changes ultimately affected all high-hazard facilities across all mission-critical sectors.

The Cullen Report[41] made more than 100 recommendations to improve safety. One of the most significant recommendations was that responsibility for identification of

Figure 4-1. The Piper Alpha platform disaster.
Source: Reproduced with permission from the Associated Press.

---

41 Lord William Cullen, *The Public Inquiry into the Piper Alpha Disaster* (London: Her Majesty's Stationery Office, 1990), http://www.hse.gov.uk/offshore/piper-alpha-disaster-public-inquiry.htm.

major accident risks should be transferred from legislator and safety inspectorate to the operating company. Since then, safety has been established as the number one priority for companies operating in high-hazard environments. The management of safety risk is now a key activity embedded into every process.

Defining Safety Risk

In safety, the definition of risk is: "a measure of human injury, environmental damage, or economic loss in terms of both the incident likelihood and the magnitude of the loss or injury."[42]

In a high-hazard environment, typical consequences of an incident include the following:

- **Death or injury** – To personnel or, in some cases, to members of the public

- **Harm to the environment** – For instance, a release of oil or gas due to a loss of containment

- **Equipment damage** – To expensive industrial plant machinery such as turbines or transformers that may take months to replace

- **Loss of production** – Which could result from equipment damage or other process failures

- **Regulatory violations** – Stemming from one or more of the other consequences

- **Brand damage** – Again, as a result of one or more of the other consequences

Companies will assess the likelihood and consequence (magnitude, severity) of safety risks and plot them on a risk matrix. A generic example is shown in Figure 4-2. Each industry and company customizes its risk matrix to suit its business and the associated risks.

This method of quantifying risks enables management to understand the risks they face and where they must focus resources to minimize these risks. In this example, the four levels of likelihood and four levels of consequence are combined to produce a number from 1 to 16, with 1 being the least amount of risk and 16 being the highest. The colors indicate categorization of these risks with green representing minor risks that require very little oversight, orange representing moderate risks that need

---

42 Definition from the American Institute of Chemical Engineers (AIChE) and Center for Chemical Process Safety (CCPS).

							Likelihood			
Consequence							Improbable (> 10 years)	Remote (Once in 10 years)	Occasional (Once a year)	Frequent (Once a month)
		Health & Safety	Environmental	Financial	Reputation & Public Disruption	Regulatory	1	2	3	4
Low	1	Injury or illness without a loss of a work day; Event requiring First Aid	Unfavorable impact but without any environmental harm or nuisance	Less than $10k	Public not aware	Limited impact with less than $10k in fines or penalties	1	2	3	4
Moderate	2	Injury or illness resulting in treatment by a doctor or hospitalization; Long term sickness over 3 days	Unreasonable impact resulting in environmental nuisance/cleanup	Between $10k and $100k	Local media coverage; Telephone complaints	Fines or penalties between $10k and $200k	2	4	6	8
High	3	Permanent injury or long term sickness over 3 months; Multiple serious injuries	Significant impact with localized environmental harm but not in an environmentally sensitive area	Between $100k and $1m	Extended local adverse media campaign; State media coverage	Fines or penalties between $200k and $500k	3	6	9	12
Severe	4	Single or multiple deaths; Multiple permanent injuries	Major environmental harm caused in environmentally sensitive areas; Environmental damage causing a violation of law or regulation	Over $1m	National adverse media coverage	Officer jailed Fine or penalty over $500k	4	8	12	16

Figure 4-2. Example risk matrix.

additional attention, and red representing extreme risks that must be stopped or miti-gated to the moderate or minor level.

Defining Cybersecurity Risk

In cybersecurity, risk is defined as "an expression of the likelihood that a defined threat will exploit a specific vulnerability of a particular attractive target or combination of targets to cause a given set of consequences."

In an information-management environment, typical consequences include:

- **Loss of sensitive information** – Either for personnel (e.g., employee person-ally identifiable information—PII) or customers (e.g., banking or credit card information)

- **Loss of proprietary information** – Intellectual property, for example

- **Loss of service** – Which could be as a result of destructive malware (e.g., ran-somware) or a denial-of-service (DoS) attack[43]

- **Regulatory violations** – Stemming from one or more of the other consequences

- **Brand damage** – Again, as a result of one or more of the other consequences

---

43 A denial-of-service (DoS) attack occurs when legitimate users are unable to access information sys-tems, devices, or other network resources due to the actions of a malicious cyber threat actor. US Cybersecurity and Infrastructure Security Agency (CISA), "Security Tip (ST04-015): Understanding Denial-of-Service Attacks," revised November 20, 2019, accessed June 21, 2021, https://us-cert.cisa. gov/ncas/tips/ST04-015.

Threat event	Vulnerability	Security control	Likelihood of threat	Degree to which control is implemented	Worst case business process impact (Confidentiality)	Worst case business process impact (Availability)	Residual risk score (Confidentiality)	Residual risk score (Availability)	Residual risk score (Overall)
Human error	Lack of appropriate level of security controls	Information assets that are processed, stored, or transmitted are handled in accordance with classification level	100%	4	3	3	1	1	2
Unauthorized network or system access	Lack of appropriate level of security controls	Data encryption and authentication requirements are based on classification level	100%	3	3	3	1	1	2
DDoS or DoS attack	Business continuity or disaster recovery plan fails to meet the recovery time objectives	A comprehensive business continuity plan defines the recovery process to meet the objectives	100%	3	3	3	2	2	

Figure 4-3. Typical information security risk assessment example.

In most companies, management of cybersecurity risk tends to rest with IT depart-ments. As a result, cybersecurity risks are often quantified by methods other than those established in safety. Figure 4-3 shows a typical example. In this case, the list of consequences has been distilled into two main impacts: Confidentiality (e.g., loss of information) and Availability (loss of service). Although there are some similarities with the safety approach shown in Figure 4-2 (such as the use of "likelihood" and "consequence" to categorize each risk), the approach is not consistent.

Industrial Cybersecurity Risk

Industrial cybersecurity risks are unique, as they combine threats related to infor-mation security (destructive malware, DoS attacks) with the consequences related to safety (death or injury, harm to the environment, damage to equipment).

For companies solely concerned with information security, a methodology that results in the assessment shown in Figure 4-3 will work well. However, companies with industrial cybersecurity risks must ensure they incorporate industrial cybersecurity risk management into their safety methodology. It is essential that industrial cyberse-curity risks are managed in the same way as safety risks.

Consider the gas turbine control system example from Chapter 2, "What Makes Industrial Cybersecurity Different?" The cybersecurity risks associated with the gas turbine control system are as follows:

- Malicious modification of PLC code, which causes the turbine to operate out-side the normal envelope while reporting normal conditions to the operator and product supplier

- Deployment of destructive malware or unauthorized remote access on a human-machine interface (HMI), which causes loss of view or control or enables control by an unauthorized user

- Fire and gas controller disabled by malware or code modification, which results in failure to shut down the turbine in unsafe conditions

All three of these scenarios have occurred in industry.

In 2010, malware called Stuxnet was operating in a nuclear enrichment facility in Iran. The purpose of the malware was to modify PLC code to run centrifuges outside their normal operating envelope but report normal conditions to the operators. This malware caused millions of dollars of damage to centrifuge equipment and set back the Iranian nuclear enrichment program.[44,45]

In December 2015, attackers took control of operator workstations in three Ukrainian power distribution companies and were able to disable power to over 225,000 customers for up to six hours. It was later discovered that the attackers gained access to the companies' networks at least six months earlier.[46]

In August 2017, an attack on a safety system in a petrochemical facility in the Middle East led to a plant shutdown. Although there were no injuries or harm to the environment, the shutdown resulted in a loss of production as well as additional unscheduled time, cost, and risk involved with restarting the plant. It was later discovered there had been a prior attempt to interfere with the same safety system in June 2017. One of the most significant factors in this incident was a failure of people and process. The safety system controller was in *program* mode (set using a physical key on the controller). Had the key been in *run* mode, it would not have been possible to modify the code.[47]

As noted in Chapter 2, it remains difficult to convince those with the ability to take action—either leadership who can provide the resources, or individuals who can take their own mitigating actions—of the potential consequences of cybersecurity incidents in an industrial environment. Elevating industrial cybersecurity risks to the same level as safety risks makes them clearly visible to everyone in the company and

---

44 Ralph Langer, *To Kill a Centrifuge: A Technical Analysis of What Stuxnet's Creators Tried to Achieve*, accessed June 21, 2021 (Arlington, VA: The Langner Group, November 2013), https://www.langner.com/wp-content/uploads/2017/03/to-kill-a-centrifuge.pdf.

45 Nicholas Falliere, Liam O Murchu, and Eric Chen, *W32.Stuxnet Dossier Version 1.3* (November 2010), accessed June 21, 2021, https://www.wired.com/images_blogs/threatlevel/2010/11/w32_stuxnet_dossier.pdf.

46 Amy Krigman, "Cyber Autopsy Series: Ukrainian Power Grid Attack Makes History," GlobalSign Blog, October 22, 2020, accessed June 21, 2021, https://www.globalsign.com/en/blog/cyber-autopsy-series-ukranian-power-grid-attack-makes-history.

47 Dragos, "TRISIS Malware: Analysis of Safety System Targeted Malware," version 1.20171213, accessed June 21, 2021, https://www.dragos.com/wp-content/uploads/TRISIS-01.pdf.

forces senior management to treat them as they would a safety risk, in particular, by taking the following actions:

- Assess the risk before undertaking any work.

- Establish and maintain controls to mitigate the likelihood and/or consequence of the risk.

- Empower individuals to intervene and, if necessary, stop work if insecure behavior is being exhibited.

As Low as Reasonably Practicable

The phrase *as low as reasonably practicable* (ALARP) originates from health and safety legislation developed in the UK, specifically the 1974 Health and Safety at Work Act. This act requires "the provision and maintenance of plant and systems of work that are, so far as is reasonably practicable, safe and without risks to health." This leads to the requirement that risks are reduced to ALARP. This practice was first tested in UK case law with the case of Edwards versus the National Coal Board in 1949. The ruling was as follows:

> "Reasonably practicable" is a narrower term than "physically possible" … a computation must be made by the owner in which the quantum of risk is placed on one scale and the sacrifice involved in the measures necessary for averting the risk (whether in money, time, or trouble) is placed in the other, and that, if it be shown that there is a gross disproportion between them – the risk being insignificant in relation to the sacrifice – the defendants discharge the onus on them.[48]

ALARP is widely used in safety standards and legislation throughout the world. IEC 61508[49] defines the following for risks:

- Zero risk can never be reached; only probabilities can be reduced.

- Non-tolerable risks must be reduced (ALARP).

- Optimal, cost-effective safety is achieved when addressed in the entire safety life cycle.

Figure 4-4 shows a visual representation of ALARP. Initially minimal cost (or effort equated to cost) is expended to mitigate significant or intolerable risk. As risk is

---

48 "ALARP at a glance," Health and Safety Executive, accessed November 6, 2021, https://www.hse.gov.uk/managing/theory/alarpglance.htm.

49 IEC 61508-1:2010, *Functional Safety of Electrical/Electronic/Programmable Electronic Safety-Related Systems – Part 1: General Requirements* (IEC [International Electrotechnical Commission]).

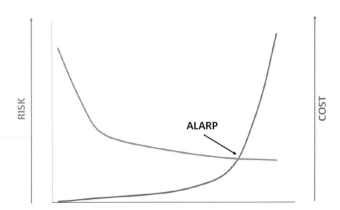

Figure 4-4. Visualizing ALARP.

addressed, the cost to mitigate increases further. The ALARP point is when the cost to mitigate additional risk becomes disproportional to the risk reduction.

The ALARP concept can be applied equally well to managing cybersecurity risk, and especially to industrial cybersecurity risk. Consider the fact mentioned in Chapter 1, that investment in cybersecurity spending is forecasted to reach $172 billion in 2022[50]. Despite this massive investment, organizations are still being impacted by cybersecurity incidents that, with hindsight, could have been easily prevented. The following examples were discussed previously: The fuel pipeline company that was incapacitated by ransomware because of an inadequately secured remote access connection; the water treatment plant that was tampered with by a disgruntled former employee who still had access to systems; the compromise of a safety controller that could have been prevented by turning a physical key to a different position.

These incidents illustrate the fact that too little effort is made to address intolerable risks that, ironically, involve minimal cost. While it is unclear if the current investment is appropriate, it is clearly not correctly targeted.

Security Process Hazard Analysis

Edward Marszal and Jim McGlone have developed a solution to ensure that industrial cybersecurity risks are treated in the same way as safety risks: the security PHA review, or SPR (pronounced *spur*). Their book *Security PHA Review for Consequence-Based*

---

50 "Cybersecurity spending trends for 2022: Investing in the future," CSO, Accessed February 14, 2022, https://www.csoonline.com/article/3645091/cybersecurity-spending-trends-for-2022-investing-in-the-future.html

Cybersecurity[51] highlights the limitations of existing cybersecurity risk assessment methodologies and details the SPR methodology. SPR reuses the principles of safety risk assessment already in place. As the authors note: "the process industries have already established methods for risk assessment that have been successfully in use for decades. The optimal solution for assessment of cybersecurity risks is not to start from scratch with new studies but to extend the existing studies to incorporate new objectives and requirements."[52]

The process hazard analysis (PHA) methodology is used to assess hazards within industrial processes. In the United States, the Occupational Safety and Health Administration (OSHA) regulates high-risk facilities using process safety management (PSM), which, among other things, requires that a PHA be conducted every five years. There are several methods for performing a PHA. Of these, the hazard and operability study (HAZOP) is the most comprehensive, systematic, and commonly used method. A variation of the HAZOP, called CHAZOP (for control hazard and operability study), was developed to assess the safety impact of control system failures.

There have been attempts to align industrial cybersecurity risk assessment with these safety methods, with cyber PHA being the most common. CHAZOP may also incorporate cybersecurity risks. However, Marszal and McGlone note that cyber PHA and CHAZOP are more akin to failure modes and effects analysis (FMEA) than HAZOP. Whereas a HAZOP focuses on the hazards in the process, cyber PHA and CHAZOP focus on control system and network equipment failure. This is not ideal because of the following:

- The frequency of cyberattack is not random like other equipment failures modeled in the FMEA. Although it is possible to apply a frequency for the purposes of analysis, there is no statistical basis for it, unlike the random hardware and human failures in non-cybersecurity assessments. The output of such an analysis is therefore misleading. This could be addressed by rigorous collection of data, but that takes time, and this issue cannot wait.

- With the focus on control system and network equipment failure, the identification of safeguards is limited to the control system and the network, whereas the overall process analysis will identify other safeguards (such as mechanical protection).

---

51 Edward Marszal and Jim McGlone, *Security PHA Review for Consequence-Based Cybersecurity* (Research Triangle Park, NC: ISA [International Society of Automation], 2019).
52 Marszal and McGlone, *Security PHA Review for Consequence-Based Cybersecurity*, 14.

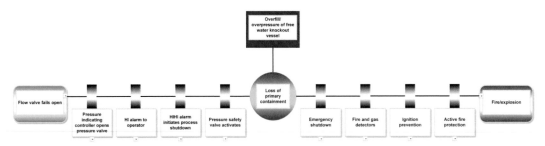

Figure 4-5. Example process safety bowtie diagram.

Figures 4-5 and 4-6 are bowtie diagrams related to safety and cybersecurity risk, respectively. Bowtie diagrams are used in safety management to help visualize the relationship between causes, hazards, and consequences.[53]

Figure 4-5 is a bowtie diagram showing a single initiating cause (flow valve fails open) resulting in a hazard (overfill/overpressure of free water knockout vessel) that causes an event (loss of primary containment) that can lead to a consequence (fire/explosion). On the left side of the diagram are preventive actions, those that are in place to stop the event (e.g., opening of a pressure valve); on the right side of the diagram are mitigating actions, those that are in place to reduce the impact of the event (e.g., emergency shutdown).

Figure 4-6 shows a typical cybersecurity bowtie. In this case, the initiating cause (malware deployed on system) leads to a generic hazard (cybersecurity threat), event

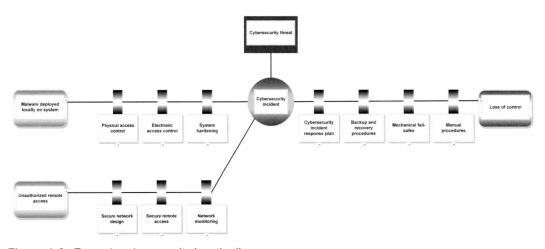

Figure 4-6. Example cybersecurity bowtie diagram.

---

53 It is not the aim of this book to describe the bowtie diagram in detail. The "Further Reading" section provides references for more details on this subject.

(cybersecurity incident), and ultimately a consequence (loss of control), which is system, rather than process, focused. As a result, the preventive and mitigating actions are focused on the system rather than the process.

Figure 4-7 shows a simplified overview of the SPR process. The beauty of the process is that the SPR is either part of an overall PHA study or uses the output of a PHA study. This elevates cybersecurity in the overall process, where it can be properly addressed. The company's safety organization must understand that cybersecurity risks can contribute to process hazards, and they should not be treated as unrelated issues to be managed by others in the company. This is easier said than done: Plant-based OT personnel may not have the time or resources to address these issues. IT personnel may not have the domain knowledge to properly appreciate the issues.

Each scenario of the PHA is reviewed to determine whether it is *hackable*. This is a commonly used term in IT security, but in the SPR process it means that "the scenario could be forced to occur by a malevolent actor who has taken control of the ICS [industrial

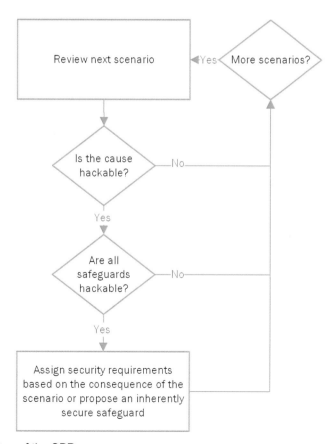

Figure 4-7. Overview of the SPR process.

Table 4-1. Simplified causes, consequences, and safeguards from a gas turbine PHA.

Cause	Consequence	Safeguard
Loss of turbine wash water feed pump suction	Pump damage	Low-flow alarm
Loss of lube oil cooling	Bearing damage	High-temperature alarm
Overpressure of HP separator	Loss of containment, release of production fluids resulting in fire/explosion	Pressure safety valve

control system]."[54] The cause or initiating event is reviewed first. The assumption is that computer-related causes can be hacked, but mechanical-related causes cannot.

If a cause can be hacked, the safeguards are then reviewed to determine if they can also be hacked. Again, the assumption is that all computer- or electronic-related safeguards can be hacked, but mechanical devices such as relief valves cannot.

Table 4-1 shows a simplified list of causes, consequences, and safeguards from a gas turbine PHA. In this case, the loss of turbine wash-water feed-pump suction and loss of lube oil cooling would be hackable because the safeguards relate to computer-based elements, and the overpressure of a high-pressure (HP) separator would not, because its safeguard is mechanical.

From a cybersecurity perspective, the concern is warranted only when a cause and all the related safeguards can be hacked. If a cause, or any one of the safeguards for that cause, cannot be hacked, no further action is required from a cybersecurity perspective.

For each hackable scenario, there are two options:

1. Assign security requirements based on the consequence category from the PHA and the risk tolerance of the process owner.

2. Identify a *nonhackable* safeguard that can be introduced, that is, an inherently secure safeguard such as a pressure-relief device or check valve. Note that some previously inherently secure safeguards, such as an overspeed trip, may now be digital and thus could be hackable.

To quantify the security requirements, the SPR process uses security levels (SLs) defined in the ISA/IEC 62443 Series. The standards define five different security levels, each with an increasing level of security demand:

---

54 Marszal and McGlone, *Security PHA Review for Consequence-Based Cybersecurity,* 9.

- **SL-0** – No specific requirements or security protection necessary

- **SL-1** – Protection against casual or coincidental violation

- **SL-2** – Protection against intentional violation using simple means with low resources, generic skills, and low motivation

- **SL-3** – Protection against intentional violation using sophisticated means with moderate resources, industrial automation and control system (IACS) specific skills, and moderate motivation

- **SL-4** – Protection against intentional violation using sophisticated means with extended resources, IACS-specific skills, and high motivation

A security level is analogous to a safety integrity level (SIL) that is used to define the performance required for a safety instrumented function (SIF). There are four levels for SIL, from 1 to 4, where 4 is the most dependable. The use of SL further helps to embed cybersecurity risks into the overall process, as those involved in safety management can appreciate the analogy to the SIL.

Quantifying Risks with Statistics

Monte Carlo Simulation

Embedding cybersecurity risks into the PHA process helps the organization acknowledge them and deal with them in the same way that it deals with other safety-related risks.

Methods to integrate cybersecurity risks into existing risk management programs have had limited success to date. One of the issues is that most risk management programs use a qualitative estimate of risk (e.g., low/medium/high or ranked 1 to 5). The cybersecurity community has concerns about providing such estimates for cybersecurity incidents.

Consider the matrix shown in Figure 4-2. The severity rating is classified in different consequence types (health and safety, environmental, financial, reputation and public disruption, and regulatory) and categorized with terms from Low up to Severe. The likelihood is categorized in terms of the frequency of occurrence, from Improbable (less than 10 years) to Frequent (once a month). The common criticisms of this method from the cybersecurity community are as follows:

- There is insufficient data on cybersecurity incidents to accurately estimate likelihood.

- Although it may be possible to estimate a financial loss, there is some skepticism that a cybersecurity incident could directly lead to consequences such as injury, death, or damage to the environment.

There is also a genuine concern about such matrices as they can produce confusing or contradictory results if poorly defined. For instance, in the risk matrix in Figure 4-2, a financial consequence of less than $10,000 is considered low, whereas a loss of more than $1,000,000 is seen as severe. However, if the low consequence event occurred frequently (once a month) it could cost the organization more than the severe-rated consequence.

Douglas Hubbard and Richard Seiersen offer methods to provide qualified estimates in their book *How to Measure Anything in Cybersecurity Risk*. Contrary to the concerns about estimating risk, they point out: "There are problems in statistics that can only be solved by using a probabilistically expressed prior state of uncertainty."[55]

Hubbard and Seiersen propose a method involving Monte Carlo simulation, where a large number (hundreds of thousands or even millions) of scenarios are run to predict the likelihood of a particular event. The origin of Monte Carlo simulation, to solve problems related to the first atomic bomb, demonstrates the usefulness in estimating events with minimal or, in this case, no prior history.

Using Hubbard and Seiersen's method, it is possible to calculate an estimated range, for instance, the financial impact of a cybersecurity incident, together with a *confidence interval*. This confidence interval, expressed as a percentage, represents the level of certainty that the financial impact will be within the estimated range. The outcome of the process is a *loss exceedance curve*, similar to that shown in Figure 4-8. The loss exceedance curve plots the results from the Monte Carlo simulation to show the probability of loss across a range of values. Using the curve, it is possible to obtain the probability that a loss will exceed a certain amount. The loss exceedance curve can show the following:

- **Inherent risk** – This curve illustrates a situation in which no, or minimal, security controls are in place.

- **Residual risk** – This curve takes account of all security controls being in place and therefore should reduce potential losses.

---

55 Douglas W. Hubbard and Richard Seiersen, *How to Measure Anything in Cybersecurity Risk* (Hoboken, NJ: John Wiley & Sons, 2016), 38.

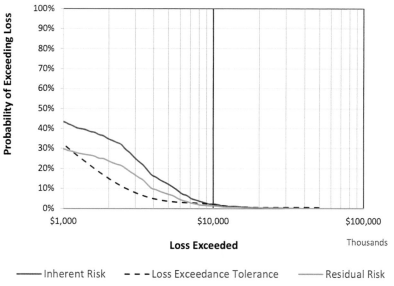

Figure 4-8. Loss exceedance curve.

- **Loss exceedance tolerance** – This curve can be used to show the organization's acceptable losses by probability of outcome to identify if additional controls are required.

Monte Carlo simulation is already widely used in organizations that are required to estimate their cybersecurity risk at a specific level of confidence, so the concept should be familiar.

- Major projects use Monte Carlo simulation to analyze cost and schedule and to produce risk-based confidence estimates, such as P10, P50, or P90, where *P* stands for *percentile*. Many organizations, such as the UK Ministry of Defense, require P10, P50, and P90 confidence forecasts to be provided.[56]

- The US Securities and Exchange Commission (SEC) defines oil and gas reserves in terms of P10, P50, and P90 ranges.[57]

Using the same ranges to quantify cybersecurity risk should provide a familiar basis for probability.

---

56 Martin Hopkinson, "Monte Carlo Schedule Risk Analysis—A Process for Developing Rational and Realistic Risk Models" (white paper, Risk Management Capability, 2011), accessed June 21, 2021, http://www.rmcapability.com/resources/Schedule+Risk+Analysis+v1.pdf.
57 "Summary Report of Audits Performed by Netherland, Sewell & Associates," accessed June 21, 2021, https://www.sec.gov/Archives/edgar/data/101778/000119312510042898/dex992.htm.

In addition to providing a qualitative estimate of the impact of a cybersecurity incident, the method provides a way to evaluate the effectiveness of cybersecurity controls. Hubbard and Seiersen call this the *return on control*, calculated using the following formula:

$$Return\ on\ Control = \frac{Reduction\ in\ Expected\ Losses}{Cost\ of\ Control} - 1^{58}$$

In the EU Network and Information Systems (NIS) directive, the correct application of this return on control is called "appropriate and proportionate."[59] This is another way of saying as low as reasonably practical (ALARP).

Hubbard and Seiersen's method is well suited to estimating the likely financial impact of a cybersecurity incident. The question is whether it can work with other consequences, such as death or injury, harm to the environment, equipment damage, loss of production, regulatory violations, and brand damage. Because these consequences all have a financial impact, one option is to estimate that impact using the loss exceedance method. The results of this method can also be used to calibrate the results from the security PHA method.

Bayes's Theorem[60]

Another statistical concept recommended by Hubbard and Seiersen is Bayes's theorem. Bayes's theorem is well suited to dealing with situations where data is limited. The challenge with statistics is that the accuracy of any estimate is based on the size of the sample. Conversely, it is impractical (or impossible) to collect a sample size sufficiently large to be accurate. Frequentist statistics, which involves the collection of sample data and estimating mean and standard deviation, works well when the data is normally distributed but is less reliable otherwise. Figure 4-9 shows a simplified example. The expectation based on frequentist statistics is the normal bell curve. Using the mean and standard deviation of this curve would indicate a remote probability of an event occurring. This could provide false reassurance.

Paul Gruhn, a renowned functional safety expert and past president of the International Society of Automation (ISA), has adopted Bayes's theorem in his work for similar reasons, "Frequentist statistics cannot be used to confirm or justify very rare events," for

---

58 Hubbard and Seiersen, *How to Measure Anything in Cybersecurity Risk*, 52.
59 European Union Agency for Cybersecurity (ENISA), "ENISA's Position on the NIS Directive," January 2016, accessed June 21, 2021, https://www.enisa.europa.eu/publications/enisa-position-papers-and-opinions/enisas-position-on-the-nis-directive.
60 This is often written as *Bayes' Theorem*. This book uses the Britannica version of the name.

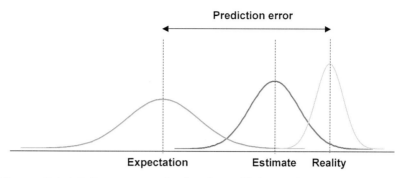

Figure 4-9. Frequentist statistics are poor at estimating unlikely events.

instance, the probability that a plant will have a catastrophic process safety accident in the next year.[61]

Bayes's theorem is explained in more detail by Gruhn and by Hubbard and Seiersen.[62] In summary, Bayes's theorem enables the re-estimation of the probability of an event occurring based on a posterior (or prior) estimate and new evidence. The formula is:

$$P(A \mid B) = \frac{P(A)P(B \mid A)}{P(B)}$$

Where P(A) and P(B) are the probabilities that two events, A and B, occur independently. P(A|B) means the probability that event A (the event we are interested in, which is hard to estimate) occurs given that event B has occurred (an event that can be observed). P(B|A) is the probability that event B occurs given that event A has occurred. What makes Bayes's theorem powerful is that P(A) can start with any prior estimate, but with new evidence (P(B), the new estimate will improve and can be used in the next iteration of the calculation when new evidence is available. To see how Bayes's theorem can help, consider the following example from Hubbard and Seiersen:

> Estimating, with limited data available, the percentage of employees who are following a procedure correctly. For example, if one can check only six people, is it possible to reliably estimate the percentage of the entire workforce who use the procedure?[63] The answer is yes if you use a beta distribution. In order to use this option, it is necessary to have a prior estimate, and then refine it based on evidence. This is where Bayes's theorem comes in.

61 Paul Gruhn, "Bayesian Analysis Improves Functional Safety," *InTech*, March 31, 2020, accessed June 21, 2021, https://www.isa.org/intech-home/2020/march-april/features/bayesian-analysis-improves-functional-safety.

62 Hubbard and Seiersen, *How to Measure Anything in Cybersecurity Risk*, 161–165.

63 Hubbard and Seiersen, 171–174.

A prior estimate can be based on data (e.g., how many people followed another procedure), or an educated guess (e.g., a specialist may use their experience to estimate the number). To be extremely conservative, the estimate could assume all probabilities are equal. This is shown in Figure 4-10. All possible probabilities are shown from 0 to 1 (or 0% to 100% in percentage terms). The uniform distribution shows all probabilities are equally valid.

If the sample set of six people is verified and determines that one of the six did not follow the procedure, it is possible to recalculate the beta distribution using the prior estimate and the new evidence. The result is shown in Figure 4-11.

This shows a 90% confidence interval that the proportion of employees who would not follow a procedure is between 5.3% and 52%. Obviously, this a wide range. This range reflects the limited number of samples. To refine the range would require more samples. However, the result is mathematically sound no matter how many samples are used.

Organizations routinely use statistical methods such as Monte Carlo simulation and Bayes's theorem for estimating business-critical factors such as project schedules and costs, and industry-specific aspects such as oil and gas reserves. Cybersecurity is another business-critical factor. Organizations should use the same proven methods to estimate its impact.

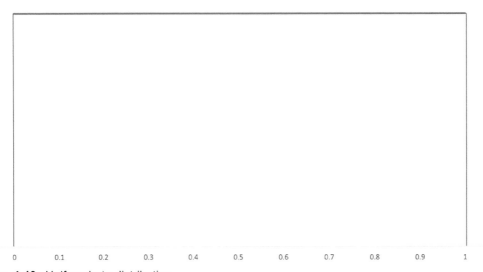

Figure 4-10. Uniform beta distribution.

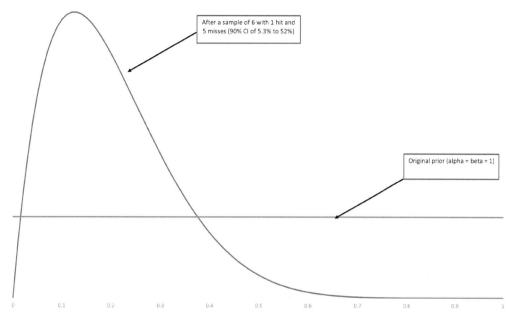

After a sample of 6 with 1 hit and
5 misses (90% CI of 5.3% to 52%)

Original prior (alpha = beta = 1)

Figure 4-11. Adjusted beta distribution after evidence is applied.

Cybersecurity Safeguards

Using ISA/IEC 62443 Standards to Define Safeguards

The ISA/IEC 62443 Series defines seven foundational requirements (FRs) that organize the technical requirements for cybersecurity management of industrial automation and control systems. These are detailed in ANSI/ISA-62443-3-3, *System Security Requirements and Security Levels:*[64]

- **FR 1** – Identification and Authentication Control (IAC)

- **FR 2** – Use Control (UC)

- **FR 3** – System Integrity (SI)

- **FR 4** – Data Confidentiality (DC)

- **FR 5** – Restricted Data Flow (RDF)

- **FR 6** – Timely Response to Events (TRE)

- **FR 7** – Resource Availability (RA)

---

64 ANSI/ISA-62443-3-3 (99.03.03)-2013, *Security for Industrial Automation and Control Systems – Part 3-3: System Security Requirements and Security Levels* (Research Triangle Park, NC: ISA [International Society of Automation]).

Each FR is first defined in terms of what is needed for each SL. For example, for FR 2, Use Control the SLs are:

- **SL-1** – Restrict use of the IACS according to specified privileges to protect against casual or coincidental misuse.

- **SL-2** – Restrict use of the IACS according to specified privileges to protect against circumvention by entities using simple means with low resources, generic skills, and low motivation.

- **SL-3** – Restrict use of the IACS according to specified privileges to protect against circumvention by entities using sophisticated means with moderate resources, IACS-specific skills, and moderate motivation.

- **SL-4** – Restrict use of the IACS according to specified privileges to protect against circumvention by entities using sophisticated means with extended resources, IACS-specific skills, and high motivation.

Each FR consists of one or more security requirements (SRs). For example, FR 2 consists of 12 SRs. Each SR consists of a base requirement plus zero or more requirement enhancements (REs) that will be required to meet increasing SLs. For example, SR 2.1, Authorization Enforcement, is one of the system requirements for FR 2 and is defined as shown in Table 4-2. The standard defines which RE(s) are required to meet each SL, for example, for SR 2.1:

- **SL-1:** SR 2.1 only

- **SL-2:** SR 2.1, RE (1) and RE (2)

Table 4-2. Requirements for SR 2.1, Authorization Enforcement.

Base Requirement	On all interfaces, the control system shall provide the capability to enforce authorizations assigned to all human users for controlling use of the control system to support segregation of duties and least privilege.
Requirement Enhancements (RE)	RE (1): Authorization enforcement for all users on all interfaces – The control system shall provide the capability to enforce authorizations assigned to all users (humans, software processes, and devices) for controlling use of the control system to support segregation of duties and least privilege. RE (2): Permission mapping to roles – The control system shall provide the capability for an authorized user or role to define and modify the mapping of permissions to roles for all human users. RE (3): Supervisor override – The control system shall support supervisor manual override of the current human user authorizations for a configurable time or event sequence. RE (4): Dual approval – The control system shall support dual approval where an action can result in serious impact on the industrial process.

- **SL-3:** SR 2.1, RE (1), RE (2), and RE (3)

- **SL-4:** SR 2.1, RE (1), RE (2), RE (3), and RE (4)

The implementation of safeguards is one part of the risk assessment process, described in ANSI/ISA-62443-3-2, *Security for Industrial Automation and Control Systems – Part 3-2: Security Risk Assessment for System Design.*[65] Figure 4-12 is a workflow diagram from the standard, showing the key steps in the process.

Once the system under consideration (SUC) is identified (i.e., what is included and excluded from the scope), an initial cybersecurity risk assessment is performed. The SUC is then divided into separate *zones* (e.g., by vendor or by functional area). Next, the connections between these zones (the *conduits*) are identified. Cybersecurity safeguards are then identified and documented. This is accomplished using the guidance from ANSI/ISA-62443-3-3 described earlier.

Implementing safeguards based on the ISA/IEC 62443 SRs enables asset owners to demonstrate traceability to an international standard. In the absence of specific regulations, such traceability helps the asset owner demonstrate that it has reduced cybersecurity risks to ALARP, much the same as traceability to International Electrotechnical Commission (IEC) 61508 requirements demonstrates management of safety risks. When combined with the SPR methodology described earlier, this traceability gives an asset owner a powerful argument for its management of cybersecurity risks.

Responsibility for Defense-in-Depth Measures

The cybersecurity bowtie diagram (such as in Figure 4-8) provides a useful visual representation of the defense-in-depth measures. These are the preventive and mitigating actions needed to manage cybersecurity risks. Within cybersecurity, responsibility for defense-in-depth measures is often shared among four principal roles:[66]

1. **Asset owner** – The organization accountable and responsible for the system

2. **Maintenance service provider** – The supplier of support activities for the system

3. **Integration service provider** – The supplier that designs, installs, configures, tests, and commissions the final system

4. **Product supplier** – The manufacturer of the system hardware and software

---

65 ANSI/ISA-62443-3-2, *Security for Industrial Automation and Control Systems – Part 3-2: Security Risk Assessment for System Design* (Research Triangle Park, NC: ISA [International Society of Automation]).
66 These principal roles are defined in ANSI/ISA-62443-1-1.

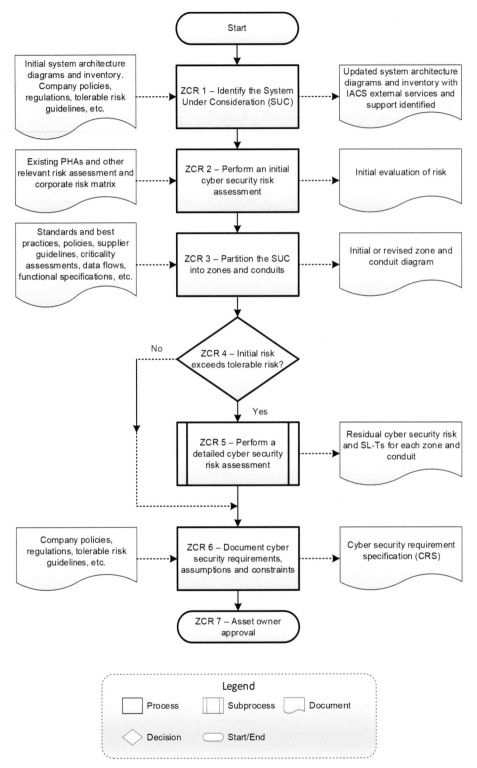

Figure 4-12. ANSI/ISA-62443-3-2, *Security for Industrial Automation and Control Systems – Part 3-2: Security Risk Assessment for System Design,* risk assessment workflow.

In some cases, the maintenance service provider, integration service provider, and product supplier may come from the same organization, the exception being providers of standard software (e.g., Windows) and hardware (e.g., network devices) which will come from other organizations.

Table 4-3 shows the typical sharing of responsibilities for the defense-in-depth measures in the bowtie diagram in Figure 4-8.

Although the asset owner has responsibility for all defense-in-depth measures, the asset owner depends on other principal roles to perform the tasks. For example:

• The asset owner can limit physical and electronic access to the system, but the maintenance service provider must do the same. In 2000, a disgruntled former contractor working for an integration service provider was able to gain unauthorized access to a wastewater control system and release raw sewage into the environment more than 40 times over several months. The integration service provider did not do enough to prevent the contractor's access. It should have, as a minimum, removed the user from the system and changed all shared account passwords when the contractor left the project.

• Removable media access, antivirus protection, operating system updates, and backup and recovery are key cybersecurity defense-in-depth measures, but they require all principal roles to contribute. The product supplier must support these features. This means, for example, not relying on an obsolete operating

Table 4-3. Responsibility for defense-in-depth measures.

Measure	Asset Owner	Maintenance Service Provider	Integration Service Provider	Product Supplier
Physical access control	X	X		
Electronic access control	X	X	X	X
Removable media access disabled	X	X	X	X
Antivirus and operating system up to date	X	X	X	X
Cybersecurity incident response plan	X	X		
Backup and recovery procedures	X	X	X	X
Mechanical fail-safes	X			
Manual procedures	X	X		

system that cannot be updated. The integration service provider must design in these requirements from the outset and test them before handover. The maintenance service provider will be required to operate these measures. This could involve taking and testing backups, as well as applying antivirus and operating system updates. The asset owner must support the measures with rules such as forbidding removable media access.

- The asset owner is entirely responsible for the mechanical fail-safes. These provide one of the last lines of protection in the event of an incident. The product supplier should not be responsible for the design or maintenance of these fail-safes. The integration service provider may design in these fail-safes (depending on its role in the project) but cannot be responsible for their maintenance and upkeep. The maintenance service provider may have some responsibility depending on its arrangement with the asset owner.

Simplified Assessment and Definition of Safeguards

At the time of writing, the asset-owner approach to industrial cybersecurity risk assessment is typically less rigorous than the SPR methodology and ISA/IEC 62443 SR compliance would provide. A typical asset owner manages industrial cybersecurity by identifying key safeguards that must be in place in any system. These are usually as follows:

- Secure network design with segregated network segments and firewalls to limit traffic to approved protocols

- Hardening of devices to remove or disable unnecessary software, services, and protocols

- Deployment of antivirus software, and ongoing upkeep of software and antivirus signatures

- Ongoing update of operating system patches

- Maintenance of system backups, establishment of recovery procedures, and routine testing of backup integrity, including verification that no malware is present in the backup

- Establishment of awareness training for all personnel

- Establishment of cybersecurity incident response plans

Asset owners typically produce specifications including these safeguards. These specifications are issued to integration service providers and product suppliers. In most cases, asset owners perform periodic audits to verify these safeguards remain in place.

Figure 4-13. IOGP lifesaving rules.

Source: Reproduced with permission from the International Association of Oil and Gas Producers (IOGP).

In many ways, these key cybersecurity safeguards mimic the lifesaving safety rules asset owners also mandate. Figure 4-13 shows the International Association of Oil & Gas Producers (IOGP) lifesaving rules that are adopted by many in that sector. Those who do not use the IOGP lifesaving rules have their own set of rules that are very similar.

The lifesaving rules set out simple and clear dos and don'ts. The rules have been put in place to ensure a consistent safety posture for all workers.

The cybersecurity safeguards achieve a similar result for the organization's cyber resources without the need to perform in-depth analysis of every system and process. If an organization can comply with all cybersecurity safeguards on all systems, the likelihood of a cybersecurity incident will be greatly reduced. The following are disadvantages of this one-size-fits-all approach:

- Systems, and the processes they control and monitor, have different levels of risk and consequence. This approach does not prioritize based on these factors.

- Systems contain different components, and as a result, it may not be possible to apply all safeguards equally across all systems.

Chapter 5, "Standardized Design and Vendor Certification," will address the issues with this approach in more detail and suggest solutions to improve it.

Another issue with the minimal set of cybersecurity safeguards is the effectiveness of the safeguard. Figure 4-14 shows the hierarchy of controls. This originated as an information note in NFPA 70E, the US National Fire Protection Association standard

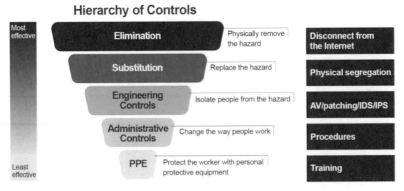

Figure 4-14. The hierarchy of controls and its relationship to cybersecurity.

for workplace electrical safety. It is now widely used to highlight the method to reduce risk, while recognizing the effectiveness of the method varies.

Figure 4-13 shows that eliminating the hazard is the most effective method, while personal protective equipment (PPE) is the least effective. If the minimum cybersecurity safeguards described earlier are mapped to the hierarchy of controls, the effectiveness of the safeguards can be seen more easily. This is shown in Table 4-4. For effectiveness, a score of 1 to 5 is used, with 1 being the least effective and 5 being the most effective.

This is especially important to understand, considering it may not be possible to deploy some safeguards on some systems. This is typically related to the engineering (more effective) measures, such as hardening and antivirus software. In these cases, asset owners end up relying on less effective safeguards (usually administrative) for the protection of the system.

Table 4-4. Effectiveness of minimum cybersecurity safeguards.

Cybersecurity Safeguard	Type of Control	Effectiveness
Secure network design, with segregated network segments and firewalls to limit traffic to approved protocols	Engineering	3
Hardening of devices to remove or disable unnecessary software, services, and protocols	Engineering	3
Deployment of antivirus software, and ongoing upkeep of software and antivirus signatures	Administrative	2
Ongoing update of operating system patches	Administrative	2
Maintenance of system backups, and establishment of recovery procedures	Administrative	2
Establishment of awareness training for all personnel	Administrative	2
Establishment of cybersecurity incident response plans	Administrative	2

The Future for Industrial Cybersecurity Risk Management

Industrial cybersecurity risk is complex. As already noted, the responsibility for managing cybersecurity safeguards is usually spread among multiple principal roles. In addition, effective cybersecurity depends on a chain of events from initial product development to operation in a facility. This cybersecurity risk chain must be understood to achieve the level of cybersecurity risk management that has been achieved in safety.

Security by design is essential to successful overall security. Consider hazardous-area equipment. An intrinsically safe device[67] is much safer to deploy than one that requires external protection (e.g., explosion-proof enclosure). The intrinsically safe device is not capable of causing an explosion. The externally protected device may explode, but the enclosure is designed to contain the explosion. A failure in the enclosure can result in a failure to contain the explosion.

With cybersecurity, locking universal serial bus (USB) ports on a workstation can be considered analogous to the enclosure option. It would be more secure to design out the USB ports, or design in some solution to make them more resilient. That would be the intrinsically safe equivalent. The USB port lock does work, but only if strict procedures are followed.

The cybersecurity risk chain, shown in Figure 4-15, identifies all the stages in the process from product design to facility operation. This is distinct from other frameworks that describe the process of a cybersecurity attack, such as Mitre's ATT&CK for

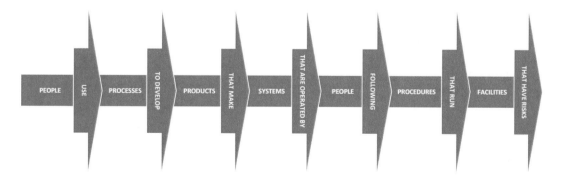

Figure 4-15. The cybersecurity risk chain.

---

67 Intrinsic safety is a design technique applied to electrical equipment for hazardous locations that is based on limiting energy, electrical and thermal, to a level below that required to ignite a specific hazardous atmospheric mixture.

Industrial Control Systems and Lockheed Martin's Cyber Kill Chain.[68,69] This cybersecurity risk chain shows how cybersecurity vulnerabilities in an operational facility are created throughout the entire system life cycle from initial product design and development to operational use.

Table 4-5 summarizes the key stages in the process and highlights what can be done to reduce the risk at each stage to reduce overall risk for the asset owner.

One notable observation from this visual representation of risk is the dominance of people and procedures. As noted throughout this book, although technology is important, the most significant factors in industrial cybersecurity are people and processes.

Table 4-5. Methods to address the industrial cybersecurity risk chain.

Stage	Issues	Methods to Address
People	• Lack of awareness of cybersecurity • No training in secure-by-design concepts	• Have certified industrial cybersecurity personnel on staff
Processes	• Lack of independence in development and testing • Lack of rigor in development and test process	• Product supplier must be certified to ANSI/ISA-62443-4-1
Products	• No common method to identify cybersecurity assurance	• Product supplier must have its products certified to ANSI/ISA-62443-4-2
Systems	• No common method to identify cybersecurity assurance • Full assessment of each system required for each project	• Product supplier must have its systems certified to ANSI/ISA-62443-3-3
People	• Lack of awareness of cybersecurity • Lack of oversight of cybersecurity issues	• Have facility certified to ANSI/ISA-62443-2-1 • Have certified industrial cybersecurity personnel on staff
Procedures	• Poor adherence to required cybersecurity safeguards • Lack of oversight of cybersecurity issues	
Facilities	• Poor adherence to required cybersecurity safeguards • Lack of oversight of cybersecurity issues	

68 The Mitre Corporation, "ATT&CK for Industrial Control Systems," accessed June 21, 2021, https://collaborate.mitre.org/attackics/index.php/Main_Page.

69 Lockheed Martin Corporation, "The Cyber Kill Chain," accessed June 21, 2021, https://www.lockheedmartin.com/en-us/capabilities/cyber/cyber-kill-chain.html.

There are already certifications in place for people, products, and systems. There will be similar certifications in place for facilities in the foreseeable future. Adoption of these certifications throughout the industrial cybersecurity risk chain would dramatically reduce cybersecurity risk for asset owners. The main issue is that asset owners are not currently demanding these certifications. Instead, asset owners are spending millions of dollars every year performing their own assessments of systems. Sometimes they assess the same system in different projects and regions. Despite this investment, the results are disappointing. As noted earlier, asset owners are satisfied with a set of minimum cybersecurity safeguards applied around the system.

Some vendors have taken the initiative to obtain certifications for their development processes, products, and systems. They promote this as a differentiator. The analogy of hazardous equipment still applies. Asset owners would not consider buying a product for use in a hazardous area unless it was certified. The future of industrial cybersecurity will be similar. Asset owners will only buy certified products and systems delivered by certified professionals.

Summary

This chapter provided details on why industrial cybersecurity risk is different from its IT counterpart. Although an increasing number of organizations understand these differences, many still use the same techniques to estimate industrial cybersecurity risk.

The security PHA method is one approach to properly recognize industrial cybersecurity risk. This approach associates incidents with the hazards in the process, unlike methods such as cyber PHA and CHAZOP that focus on control system and network equipment failure.

A common theme in cybersecurity is the reluctance to use probability and statistics to estimate cybersecurity incidents. On the surface, the lack of historical data seems to make it difficult to analyze and provide reliable estimates of future incidents. However, as noted in this chapter, "There are problems in statistics that can only be solved by using a probabilistically expressed prior state of uncertainty." Monte Carlo simulation was created to help estimate events with no prior history. Bayes's theorem enables the prediction (with appropriate confidence interval) based on any data sample size. Both can be used to provide estimates that can better target risk reduction efforts.

Risk reduction is ultimately about identifying and applying controls to reduce the likelihood and/or consequence of a cybersecurity incident. The ISA/IEC 62443 Series of

Standards provides an excellent framework on which to define cybersecurity controls using clear and consistent language. The standards also define all the stakeholders that are involved in cybersecurity management. These include the asset owner, maintenance service provider, integration service provider, and product supplier. It is essential to identify the responsibility for cybersecurity controls, especially as this responsibility is often shared among multiple stakeholders. The ISA Global Cybersecurity Alliance (ISAGCA) is a collaborative forum to advance cybersecurity awareness, education, readiness, and knowledge sharing. One key area of focus for ISAGCA is to provide guidance to industry on how to apply the ISA/IEC 62443 standards.

Even without doing a thorough risk analysis, it is still possible to apply some basic controls and make a significant improvement in cybersecurity posture. Examples abound: secure network design, hardening of devices, deployment of antivirus software, ongoing update of operating system patches, maintenance of system backups, establishment of recovery procedures, establishment of awareness training for all personnel, and establishment of cybersecurity incident response plans. These basic controls are similar to the safety rules that many organizations operate. However, like the safety rules, they rely on people following procedures, and the people or procedures can fail.

The future of cybersecurity risk management will rely more on independent assessment and certification of people, processes, and products. These certifications are almost all in place at the time of writing. But until asset owners start demanding these certifications, as they already do for other products and services, they will continue to do a lot of repetitive, expensive work to address cybersecurity risk management.

5

Standardized Design and Vendor Certification

Introduction

In response to cybersecurity threats to their products, major automation vendors have begun developing their own secure architectures. In some cases, they incorporate customized security tools. Several vendors have gone a step further and obtained third-party certification of these solutions.

Despite this, asset owners collectively spend millions of dollars designing and reviewing solutions from vendors. These solutions are routinely deployed, even within the same asset-owner organization. In fact, an asset owner with multiple projects in different regions of the world, using the same vendor solution, may treat each deployment project as if it were novel and unknown.

Clearly, more standardization would improve the owner's cybersecurity posture while reducing the cost of deployment. This chapter will consider the benefits of standardized designs, identify the elements of a standardized design, and recommend ways to capture these details and minimize implementation costs.

Benefits of Standardizing Designs

To appreciate the benefits of standardized cybersecurity designs, consider how asset owners purchase and deploy hazardous-area certified equipment.

A hazardous area is an area where the potential for an explosive or flammable atmosphere exists. Such atmospheres may exist normally (e.g., coal mines) or under fault conditions (e.g., in a petrochemical refinery where there is a leak in a tank holding flammable gas or liquid).

Equipment installed in a hazardous area is designed to operate safely in these conditions. For example, electrical or electronic equipment is designed so it cannot generate sufficient energy to ignite the explosive or flammable atmosphere. The requirements for such designs are well defined. Classification of the area, and thus the requirements for the equipment, vary. Nevertheless, hazardous-area classification provides a means to clearly define the area and its requirements.[70] Vendors must obtain and maintain third-party certification for their products used in these areas.

With these certifications in place, asset owners can select products based on the certification, confident that the hazardous-area requirements are met. The asset owner is required to follow standards and vendor instructions for safe deployment of the product, for instance, selecting the power supply or connection of external devices. These instructions are sufficiently prescriptive that there is little room for interpretation. Design documentation must be produced, but the requirements for this documentation are well defined.

Cybersecurity, by contrast, is not yet as prescriptive. Standards exist for component products[71] and systems.[72] Third-party certification against these standards can be obtained.[73] However, as of the time of this writing, asset owners do not typically require component products and systems to be certified by a third party. Instead, the asset owner defines its own internal standard for cybersecurity and assesses the vendor's solution against this standard. The asset owner still has to put additional controls in place. Despite the existence of standards for these controls, their application will vary by asset owner, and in some cases even by asset-owner site.

This current approach to cybersecurity is inefficient and produces suboptimal results:

---

70 The National Electrical Code (NEC) defines hazardous-area classifications in the United States (NEC Article 500). An NEC hazardous-area classification consists of several parts: the class, group, and division. Worldwide, outside the United States, IEC standard IEC 60079 defines hazardous-area classifications using class and zone (this classification method is known as ATEX, an abbreviation of the French *atmosphères explosibles*).

71 ANSI/ISA-62443-4-2 defines the requirements for component products; these can be embedded devices, host devices, network devices, and software applications.

72 ANSI/ISA-62443-3-3 defines the requirements for an IACS system based on security level.

73 ISASecure System Security Assurance (SSA) certifies that products have the capability to meet the requirements in ANSI/ISA-62443-3-3 and have been developed in accordance with a Security Development Lifecycle Assurance (SDLA) program. ISASecure Component Security Assurance (CSA) certifies that component products have the capability to meet the requirements in ANSI/ISA-62443-4-2 and have been developed in accordance with an SDLA program.

- The onus is on the asset owner to verify product and system compliance with cybersecurity requirements.

- The inconsistent application of standards to asset-owner facilities produces inconsistent levels of protection and requires additional effort to manage.

Standardizing designs, applying standards, and demanding certified products offer a path to overcoming these issues.

Essential Elements of a Standardized Design

Figure 5-1 shows the typical cybersecurity bowtie diagram previously discussed in Chapter 4, "Measure to Manage Cybersecurity Risk." This bowtie illustrates the mitigations required in any standardized design. It also lists other mitigations that must be in place in the environment around the system.

Recall from Chapter 4 that the ANSI/ISA-62443-3-3[74] standard defines seven foundational requirements (FRs) for industrial automation and control systems (IACSs). These, together with their objectives, are as follows:

- **FR 1, Identification and Authentication Control (IAC)** – Identify and authenticate all users (humans, software processes, and devices) before allowing them access to the control system.

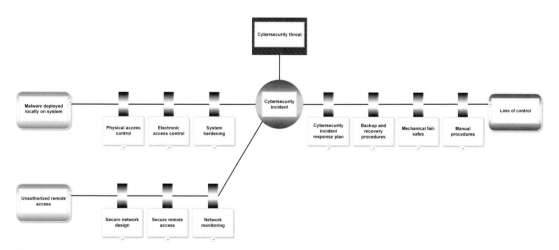

Figure 5-1. Example cybersecurity bowtie diagram.

---

74 ANSI/ISA-62443-3-3 (99.01.01)-2013, *Security for Industrial Automation and Control Systems – Part 3-3: System Security Requirements and Security Levels* (Research Triangle Park, NC: ISA [International Society of Automation]).

- **FR 2, Use Control (UC)** – Enforce the assigned privileges of an authenticated user (human, software process, or device) to perform the requested action on the IACS and monitor the use of these privileges.

- **FR 3, System Integrity (SI)** – Ensure the integrity of the IACS to prevent unauthorized manipulation.

- **FR 4, Data Confidentiality (DC)** – Ensure the confidentiality of information on communication channels and in data repositories to prevent unauthorized disclosure.

- **FR 5, Restricted Data Flow (RDF)** – Segment the control system via zones and conduits to limit the unnecessary flow of data.

- **FR 6, Timely Response to Events (TRE)** – Respond to security violations by notifying the proper authority, reporting needed evidence of the violation, and taking timely corrective action when incidents are discovered.

- **FR 7, Resource Availability (RA)** – Ensure the availability of the control system against the degradation or denial of essential services.

The mitigations shown in Figure 5-1 are derived from these FRs and are considered essential in any IACS implementation. Each IACS may require additional mitigations derived from these FRs. These requirements depend on the particular circumstances, including the security level identified for the system. This process is described in more detail in Chapter 4.

Table 5-1 summarizes the essential elements along with a reference to the ISA/IEC 62443 FRs[75] from which they are derived. The table also shows which elements relate to the system and which pertain to the environment around the system.

Table 5-1 shows why is it is not enough to implement secure systems and components. This is consistent with the hazardous-area equipment analogy already discussed. Even when a certified-hazardous-area product is procured, it must still be installed in compliance with standards and the vendor's instructions to ensure it is safe. In this case, the asset owner must put controls in place around the systems and components it procures to ensure the overall facility is secure.

Figure 5-2 shows a simplified block diagram of a typical IACS environment for a facility. This example includes an integrated control and safety system (ICSS). This could

---

75 Listed in ANSI/ISA-62443-3-3.

Table 5-1. Essential elements of a standardized design.

Mitigation	System	Environment	ISA/IEC 62443 FR Reference
Secure network design	X	X	FR 4, FR 5
System hardening	X		FR 3, FR 7
Physical access control		X	FR 1
Electronic access control	X		FR 1, FR 2
Secure remote access	X	X	FR 1, FR 2
Network monitoring		X	FR 6, FR 7
Cybersecurity incident response plan		X	FR 6
Backup and recovery procedures	X	X	FR 6, FR 7
Manual procedures		X	FR 6

also be a separate, distributed control system (DCS) and safety instrumented system (SIS), or a wide-area supervisory control and data acquisition (SCADA) system. The facility also includes a system to monitor and control the power to the plant and power to the systems themselves. These systems, along with a turbine control system, an associated vibration monitoring system, and specific control systems, are provided as part of the packaged plant system (e.g., wastewater treatment). These systems are typically procured from different vendors but must work together to achieve the overall objectives for the asset owner.

Some system vendors provide more secure solutions than others. Some offer security-specific features. A few vendors provide their own antivirus and patching solutions or their own backup solutions. Some include their own network monitoring features.

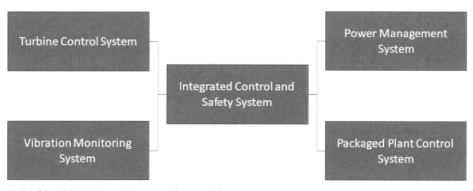

Figure 5-2. Simplified block diagram of an IACS environment.

Even with vendor support, the asset owner must secure the entire facility, not just individual systems. Maintaining multiple vendor systems for antivirus and patching could be cost prohibitive and difficult to resource. Vendors may have different standards for screening operating system patches or network monitoring, which may lead to inconsistencies. For this reason, it is essential that the scope is clearly defined. Security implementation must be facility-wide, not on a per-system basis. There are many challenges to achieving this clear scope. These challenges are discussed in more detail in Chapter 6, "Pitfalls of Project Delivery."

Figure 5-3 shows the example facility in more detail. This diagram identifies the key components of each system[76] and the connectivity required for operational purposes. The individual system architectures are based on actual vendor solutions.

The systems themselves may individually meet the asset owner's security requirements, but additional controls are required to operate in this interconnected manner.

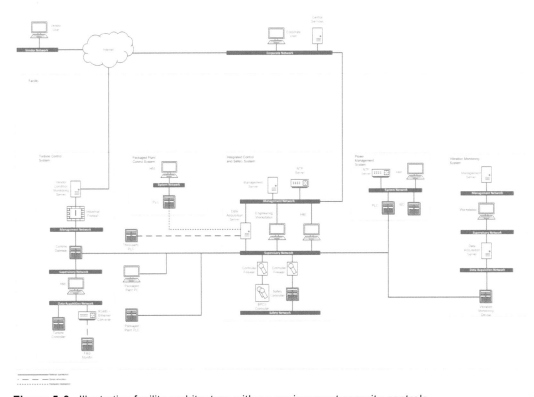

Figure 5-3. Illustrative facility architecture with no environment security controls.

---

76 The diagram is for illustrative purposes. The number of components in each system will vary depending on facility requirements.

The core of the facility is the ICSS. The other systems communicate key process data with the ICSS. This provides a facility-wide overview of operations from one human-machine interface (HMI). Each system provides its own HMI. This allows for a more detailed view of system operation. For instance, operators may require a summary of power status on the ICSS HMI. Electrical engineers may need to view more detailed power management information from that system's HMI.

The ancillary systems connect to the ICSS via Ethernet networks. Typically, the ICSS will poll the ancillary systems using an industrial protocol, such as Modbus or EtherNet/IP. This is an open standard based on the Common Industrial Protocol (CIP), not to be confused with Transmission Control Protocol/Internet Protocol (TCP/IP). The ancillary systems will return the data requested by the ICSS.

The content and operation of the packaged plant control systems vary considerably depending on the package and the vendor. In some cases, the control system may comprise a programmable logic controller (PLC) and an HMI. In other cases, it may be a personal computer (PC) connected to specialist sensors. A third option may be a PLC with no HMI. The connectivity to the ICSS will also vary. Modern packaged control systems integrate into the same Ethernet networks as the ancillary systems described earlier. However, some systems still connect using serial networks (RS-232 or RS-485). In some cases, this may involve hardwired connections, such as analog or digital inputs or outputs. These connections represent critical signals in the process.

In some facilities, it is necessary to deploy a device that belongs to a third party. A typical example is a facility operated on behalf of a government-owned oil and gas company. The government will want to receive production totals and quality informa-tion from the facility. This information is obtained from either a metering system or the ICSS, often using PLCs or remote terminal units (RTUs) connected over Ethernet or serial networks.

Secure Network Design

Creating a secure network design is the foundation to good security, but it is also the most difficult task to achieve. There are well-established methods to create secure net-work designs. ISA/IEC 62443 defines a comprehensive methodology that, if followed, greatly increases security in automation system networks. Unfortunately, few asset owners fully embrace the ISA/IEC 62443 approach. Two major challenges exist:

- Many facilities involve multiple systems from different vendors. The intrin-sic security provided varies from vendor to vendor, as does their approach to providing security safeguards. Contracts are let with individual vendors. As a result, the integration between the systems, where many security issues exist, is often overlooked.

- Network technology advances make connectivity much easier. This ease of connection opens the door to suboptimal designs with vulnerabilities that are difficult to rectify once implemented. The introduction of the Industrial Internet of Things (IIoT) inadvertently exacerbates the situation. The design intent of the IIoT neglects numerous important and beneficial architectural concepts in automation systems.

The most important concept in automation systems architecture is the Purdue hierarchy. It is critical to good security design.

Purdue Hierarchy

The Purdue hierarchy was developed by a team led by Theodore ("Ted") Williams (formerly of Monsanto Chemical Co.) at Purdue University's consortium for computer integrated manufacturing and published in 1992.[77] The Purdue reference model is part of a larger concept: the Purdue Enterprise Reference Architecture (PERA). This concept "provides a way to break down enterprises into understandable components, to allow staff at all levels to see the '20,000-ft view' as well as to describe the details that they see around them every day."[78] PERA expert and evangelist Gary Rathwell was a member of the original development team. He maintains that PERA was ahead of its time and never achieved the level of adoption that it deserved. Rathwell has successfully implemented many major automation projects by following the PERA methodology, but few outside his projects appreciate what can be achieved. Most automation professionals know only of the Purdue hierarchy, either from the ISA-95 standard, incorporated into the IEC 62264 standard, *Enterprise-Control System Integration*,[79] or the ISA-99 standard, incorporated in ISA-62443-1-1, *Security for Industrial Automation and Control Systems*,[80] and even then, there is limited understanding of the principles behind it.

Figure 5-4 shows the original Purdue hierarchy, in this case for a continuous process such as petrochemicals. Another version (with different descriptions) covered a manufacturing complex.

---

77 Theodore J. Williams, *The Purdue Enterprise Reference Architecture: A Technical Guide for CIM Planning and Implementation* (Research Triangle Park, NC: Instrument Society of America, 1992).

78 PERA Enterprise Integration (website), Gary Rathwell, accessed June 21, 2021, http://www.pera.net/.

79 IEC 62264-1:2013, *Enterprise-Control System Integration* (Geneva 20 – Switzerland: IEC [International Electrotechnical Commission]).

80 ISA-62443-1-1-2007, *Security for Industrial Automation and Control Systems – Part 1-1: Terminology, Concepts, and Models* (Research Triangle Park, NC: ISA [International Society of Automation]).

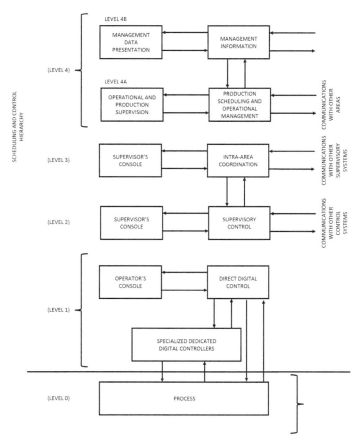

Figure 5-4. The original Purdue hierarchy.[81]

In ISA-62443-1-1, the Purdue hierarchy is used to define a contextual model. This model establishes "a frame of reference for the more detailed information that follows. It describes a generic view of an integrated manufacturing or production system."[82]

The Purdue hierarchy model in ISA-62443-1-1 includes five distinct levels. These map directly to the levels shown in Figure 5-4:

- **Level 4 (Enterprise Business Systems)** – This level includes the functions involved in the business-related activities needed to manage a manufacturing organization.

- **Level 3 (Operations Management)** – This level includes the functions involved in managing the workflows to produce the desired end products. Examples

---

81 Williams, *The Purdue Enterprise Reference Architecture*, 146.
82 ANSI/ISA-62443-1-1-2007, *Security for Industrial Automation and Control Systems*.

include dispatching production, detailed production scheduling, reliability assurance, and site-wide control optimization.

- **Level 2 (Supervisory Control)** – This level includes the functions involved in monitoring and controlling the physical process. There are typically multiple production areas in a plant or facility.

- **Level 1 (Local or Basic Control)** – This level includes the functions involved in sensing and manipulating the physical process. It includes continuous control, sequence control, batch control, and discrete control. Equipment at this level includes, but is not limited to, DCS controllers, PLCs, and RTUs. Also included in Level 1 are safety and protection systems that monitor the process and automatically return the process to a safe state if it exceeds safe limits.

- **Level 0 (Process)** – This level is the actual physical process, which includes several different types of production facilities in all sectors including, but not limited to, discrete parts manufacturing, hydrocarbon processing, product distribution, pharmaceuticals, pulp and paper, and electric power. It includes the sensors and actuators directly connected to the process and process equipment.

The ISA-62443-1-1 version of the Purdue hierarchy is shown in Figure 5-5.

The Purdue hierarchy is a foundational element for all automation systems, just as the Open Systems Interconnection (OSI) model, which defines how network systems are architected, is fundamental to all networks. An overview of the OSI model can help one better understand the importance of the Purdue hierarchy.

OSI Model

The basic reference model for OSI is a standard created in 1983 by The International Organization for Standardization (ISO) and the International Telegraph and Telephone Consultative Committee (CCITT). The standard is usually referred to as the *Open Systems Interconnection Model*, or *OSI model* for short.

The OSI model is shown in Figure 5-6. It divides network communications into seven layers:

- **Physical** – Deals with the operation of the physical connection, for example, Ethernet or Wi-Fi.

- **Data Link** – Interfaces between the logical and physical network, for example, converting between the physical hardware identifier and the configured *address* for the device.

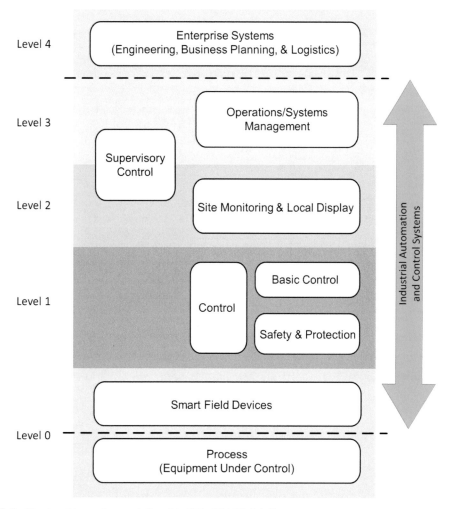

Figure 5-5. Purdue hierarchy as defined in ISA-62443-1-1.[83]

- **Network** – Routes data across networks without consideration of the data itself. The IP is used at this layer.

- **Transport** – Establishes and maintains the connection between two communicating nodes and monitors for errors. The TCP is used at this layer.

- **Session** – Coordinates and maintains communications between the two communicating nodes, including determining authorization of nodes.

- **Presentation** – Accepts application data and formats it as needed to enable it to be interpreted, including any encryption and decryption required.

---

83 ISA-62443-1-1-2007, *Security for Industrial Automation and Control Systems*, 60.

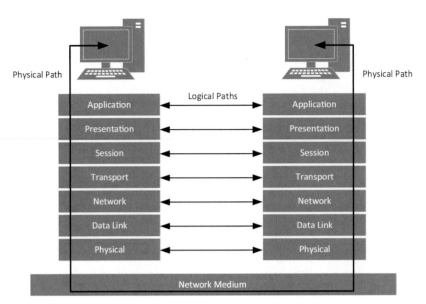

Figure 5-6. The OSI model.

- **Application** – Communicates between the lower layers of the model and the user. An example of a common application layer protocol is Hypertext Transfer Protocol (HTTP), which formats and sends requests from a web browser to a web server and shows responses from the web server on the display.

Data is transmitted to and from devices through these layers by means of protocols and services specific to each layer. The OSI model enables the use of different applications over different types of networks. For an application to run equally well on a smartphone over a cellular network, a tablet over Wi-Fi, and a desktop over Ethernet, the application must adhere to the OSI model. In this example, the OSI model separates the elements that involve interaction with the user (application, presentation), between either end of the application (session), from those that involve interaction via the network protocol (transport and network) and the physical medium (data link and physical).

Industrial protocols such as Modbus adhere to the OSI model. This enables Modbus-based applications to communicate with serial devices over RS-232 or RS-485, as well as devices on Ethernet or Wi-Fi.

IIoT and the Purdue Reference Model

Some consider the Purdue hierarchy obsolete. Key drivers behind this opinion are the growing adoption of the IIoT and the move to locate central processing servers to the cloud.

Definitions of IIoT are many and varied. In general, the concept differs from conventional automation systems. Sensors and actuators are connected directly to systems,

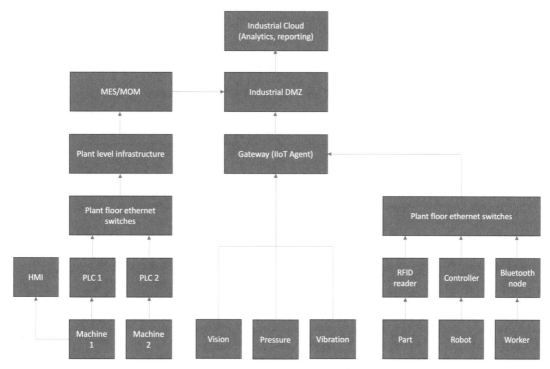

Figure 5-7. Example of a cloud-oriented industrial architecture.[84]

typically cloud-based, which "allows for a higher degree of automation by using cloud computing to refine and optimize the process controls."[85]

Figure 5-7 shows an example of a cloud-oriented industrial architecture. This alternative to the Purdue hierarchy is intended to demonstrate why it is no longer applicable.

This diagram, and the associated argument, demonstrate a common misunderstanding of the Purdue hierarchy.

The Purdue hierarchy is a logical, or functional, hierarchy rather than a physical one. In the PERA,[86] Williams identifies the key reasons behind a functional hierarchy:

- Levels reduce the size and complexity of the problem.

- Levels limit the scope of responsibility and authority.

84 "Is the Purdue Model Dead?"
85 "Industry 4.0," University of West Florida (website), accessed June 21, 2021, https://uwf.edu/centers/haas-center/industrial-innovation/industry-40/.
86 Williams, *The Purdue Enterprise Reference Architecture*, 144.

- Levels differentiate between the length of the planning horizon and the required speed of response.

- Moving down the hierarchy, the planning horizon decreases while required speed of response increases.

The example in Figure 5-7 is a mixture of functional (e.g., machine operations) and physical (e.g., plant floor Ethernet switches) elements. This figure makes the implicit assumption that placing applications (e.g., inventory tracking) in the cloud affects the hierarchy. Again, this decision concerns the physical, not functional, elements and has no bearing on the hierarchy.

Hierarchy and Speed of Response

The length of planning horizon and the speed of response are particularly relevant to automation system cybersecurity. These factors impact reliability and availability. Figure 5-8 shows the Purdue hierarchy from ISA-62443-1-1 overlaid with an example time-base for speed of response. Time-bases may vary from sector to sector, system to system, and facility to facility. An electrical control system, for instance, requires a more rapid speed of response than does a wastewater control system. Figure 5-8 shows how the speed of response varies at each level. This feature helps determine where functionality should lie. Because the architecture in Figure 5-7 does not follow the Purdue hierarchy, it cannot be used to confirm if the design choices meet the functional requirements.

A key application for many asset owners and their vendors is condition-based monitoring. Condition-based monitoring requires data at a relatively low rate and assumes the condition does not change rapidly. The primary use of condition-based monitoring is to monitor operational data over time. The goal is to predict failures, rather than detect issues, in near real time. Figure 5-9 shows that both of these solutions achieve the condition-based monitoring application requirement.

An example of the additional sensors mentioned in Figure 5-7 could be vision, pressure, and vibration. These sensors are assumed to be IIoT devices. That means they connect to an IIoT gateway that serves data to applications in the cloud. Conventional industrial sensors would connect to a DCS, which then serves data to the same applications via, typically, a historian.

Consider the vibration sensor as an example. Although vibration data may be used for longer time-horizon requirements such as condition-based monitoring, the same sensors will normally generate alarms requiring immediate attention—for instance,

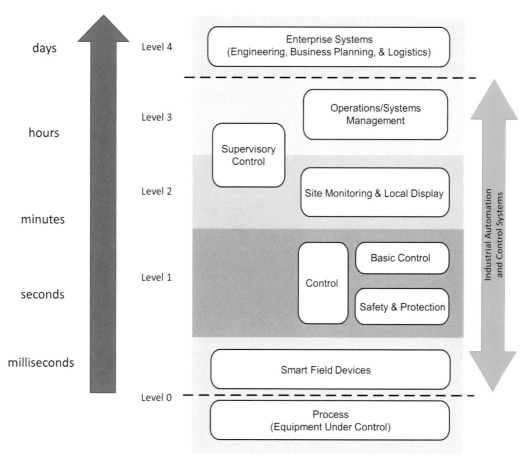

Figure 5-8. Speed of response and planning horizon across levels.

overspeed and bearing temperature. This requirement cannot be met by the IIoT solution. It lacks Level 1 or Level 2 functionality, meaning the connection to the DCS controller and visibility to the operator on the DCS HMI. In most facilities, there would also be a hardwired connection from the vibration monitoring system to a safety system. This feature enables an emergency shutdown independent of the DCS operator. For the example described, the option on the right in Figure 5-9 is the only one that meets all the requirements.

It is hard to imagine a scenario where the additional sensor examples shown (vision, pressure, vibration) would not require such an architecture to meet all operational requirements.

Some of the sensors shown in Figure 5-7 do not fall into this category: The parts tracking functionality (radio-frequency identification and barcode readers) is unlikely to

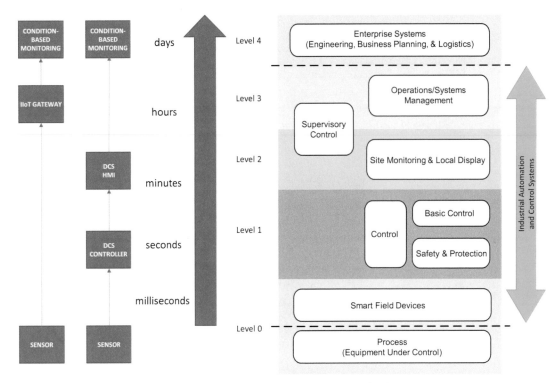

Figure 5-9. Conventional and IIoT-based approach to vibration monitoring.

require responses in the millisecond, second, or minute timescales. For these, an IIoT solution will likely be acceptable.

The worker monitoring requirements are unclear. If there is physiological monitoring (body temperature, heart rate, blood pressure) or location tracking, then it may be important to generate an alarm in the control room. These conditions may be tracked elsewhere, for example, by medical staff in a separate location. If so, only a periodic summary would be provided to the control room.

Hierarchy and Control

The advent of IIoT and cloud computing in automation has led to some misleading ideas regarding user requirements in network designs. As noted earlier, IIoT "allows for a higher degree of automation by using cloud computing to refine and optimize the process controls." This statement is reasonable; Figure 5-10 shows how it would be realized. The traditional, closed-loop control arrangement involves several steps. First, it compares a set point (desired value) to a measured value. Then it uses the difference (the actuating variable) to provide an input to a controller. The controller

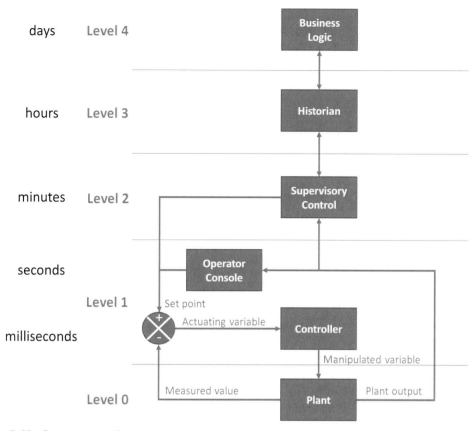

Figure 5-10. Control in the Purdue hierarchy.

produces an output (the manipulated variable) that drives the plant toward minimizing the difference.

In traditional implementations, the set point is set locally via the operator console or the supervisor control console. The advent of improved communications and devices allows a "higher degree of automation." This enables some business logic to determine the optimal set points needed to achieve a particular objective. However, the use of IIoT cannot change where the closed-loop control is executed, at least not in a resilient solution. The Purdue levels help explain the order of priority for operation:

- **Level 0** – The plant must be able to either operate safely without Level 1 or be shut down in the event of a loss of level 1 (local control).

- **Level 1 and below** – The plant must be able to operate without Level 2 (supervisory control).

- **Level 2 and below** – The plant must be able to operate without Level 3 (historian).

- **Level 3 and below** – The plant must be able to operate without Level 4 (business logic).

The introduction of IIoT has led to misunderstandings about the Purdue hierarchy. These misunderstandings have enabled the creation of architectures that are not resilient against common failure modes. These modes include loss of wide area network connectivity and failure of supervisory console.

Consider a water treatment plant influent control system. Figure 5-11 presents two options. The first option (left) is simpler. It includes a plant control/monitoring function communicating directly with a SCADA function for operator display. This setup enables onward communication to a historian function for use in reporting within the business. The second option (right) splits the data acquisition function in two, with a plant data logging function on-site and the same SCADA function as before.

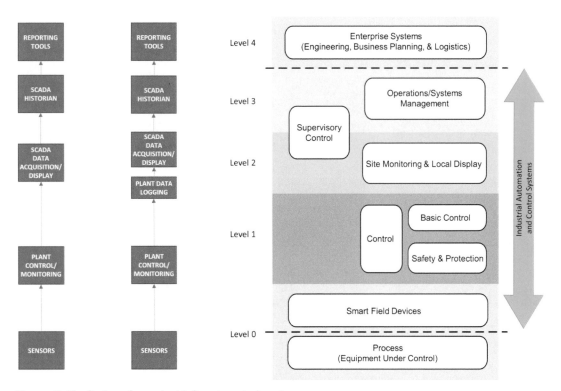

Figure 5-11. Options for a plant influent control system.

The optimal solution will depend on the detailed functional requirements. In many cases, some requirements are overlooked and the wrong solution is selected. In this example, one requirement is to log the result of chlorine contact time calculations for regulatory purposes. Failure to log the data may result in regulatory action, including fines. Consider the following failure scenarios:

- Loss of communications between the site and SCADA data acquisition

- Failure of the SCADA data acquisition

- Loss of communications between SCADA data acquisition and the SCADA historian

- Failure of the SCADA historian

Without plant data logging, any of these scenarios could lead to a loss of regulatory data, or a site visit to manually record this data. Depending on system configuration, some scenarios may avoid this situation. For example, if the SCADA can store data for several days, then loss of communications with the historian, or failure of the historian, may not present a problem. Nevertheless, a good design that incorporates the plant data logging function would mitigate this risk in all cases. The weaker design may cost a bit less, but this savings would be erased by the fines and overtime costs for a single failure.

Compare the facility architecture shown in Figure 5-3 with the equivalent Purdue hierarchy shown in Figure 5-12.

Considering the impact of failure scenarios on availability, solutions to achieve required levels of availability are key to a good design. This will be discussed in more detail later in this chapter.

Zones and Conduits

Network segmentation is an important defense strategy. Large, *flat* networks with everything connected create more opportunities for unauthorized access to systems. Once an attacker enters a network, it has access to everything at once. Dividing a network into segments, and controlling the flow of traffic between these segments, mitigates this risk.

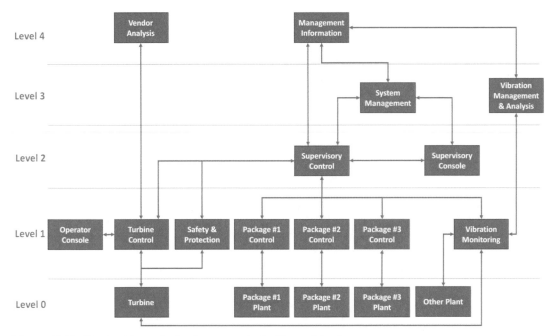

Figure 5-12. Purdue hierarchy for the example facility architecture.

The ANSI/ISA-62443-3-3 standard defines the concept of zones and conduits for the purposes of network segmentation. The standard defines the terms as follows:

- **Zone** – A grouping of assets that share the same cybersecurity requirements

- **Conduit** – A grouping of assets dedicated exclusively to communications and that share the same cybersecurity requirements

Zones

Zones can be created based on logical or physical groupings of equipment. Whatever grouping is defined, the equipment within that zone should have a common set of security requirements. Examples include the following:

- A zone for each remote site in a network

- A zone for each production process within a site

- Separate safety and control zones

- Separate vendor control systems

Zones can have sub-zones. For instance, a production-process zone may be broken down into individual sub-zones related to specific, separate functions.

The Demilitarized Zone

The demilitarized zone (DMZ) is a particular zone used in secure designs. The name comes from its use in agreements between nations that define boundaries between two or more military powers or alliances. One of the most famous DMZs is the area between North and South Korea.

In computer networks, a DMZ is a network zone that separates *trusted* and *untrusted* networks. A typical IT example is the separation of a company intranet (the trusted network) from the Internet (the untrusted network). In this scenario, the DMZ provides an additional layer of security: internal resources on the intranet are not directly connected to the Internet, where they could be more easily accessed. Instead, the internal resources connect to resources in the DMZ, and resources in the DMZ connect to the Internet. A simplified block diagram of a DMZ arrangement is shown in Figure 5-13.

A key element of a DMZ is the deployment of shared services, such as email, network time, and the domain name system (DNS). This feature can greatly improve automation system network designs if implemented correctly.

For example, note in Figure 5-3 that there are two Network Time Protocol (NTP) servers shown, one as part of the ICSS and one as part of the Power Management System. The additional servers, antennas, and associated cabling impact capital and operational costs with no added benefit. A better solution would be to provide a centrally

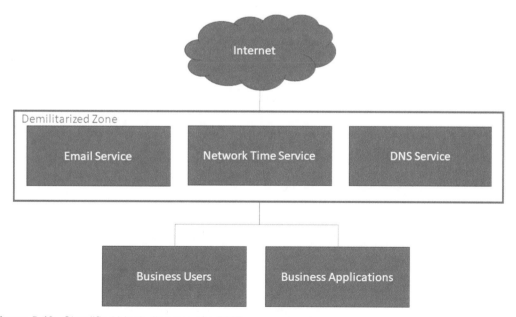

Figure 5-13. Simplified block diagram of a DMZ arrangement.

managed NTP service in the DMZ. This would enable all equipment to share the same resource. The result is cheaper and easier to manage.

Additional services that could be shared between systems include the following:

- **Access control** – Some automation system vendors utilize full Windows domain services for authentication and authorization. This approach supports system-wide management of users, including enforcement of security requirements such as password complexity and update. Some vendors still rely on very basic Windows features such as workgroups. These features only provide for peer-to-peer networking and do not include system-wide user management. Even if multiple systems use Windows domain services, they often use their own implementations. This leads to a duplication of effort. A more logical option would be a centrally managed domain service configured for a single list of users. This would provide access to the automation systems each user requires for their role. Each user would manage a single password. Removing former users from multiple systems would require only one activity. Changing access rights is also greatly simplified when centrally managed.

- **Remote access** – Automation system vendors offer a range of standard and custom methods for remote access to their systems. Some use standard Windows remote desktop services. Others use third-party products. Still others develop their own web-based methods. This array of remote access options creates a maintenance and security challenge. Denying remote access to systems can create its own security challenges. Users often find ways around these restrictions. A better option is to provide a standard method of remote access, through services in the DMZ. This approach gives authorized users one path of access to the systems they need.

- **Antivirus and patching** – Because the majority of automation system workstations and servers are Windows-based, protecting against malware and operating system vulnerabilities is critical. Most automation system vendors now support antivirus and operating system updates (*patches*). Many use standard solutions to support these, such as endpoint security solutions from reputable vendors. Vendors often provide their own system-wide endpoint security and upgrade management. This practice duplicates equipment and requires additional maintenance. These services are all based on central management and would logically fit in the DMZ model.

- **Backup and recovery** – Backup requirements vary considerably for automation systems. In some cases, backups of server and workstation images are required only when configuration changes are made. In other cases, backups of data are also necessary. As with other services, automation system vendors may provide their own solutions for backup. Irrespective of individual requirements, it makes sense to centralize all backups in one location. This aids with transfer to an off-site location, as well as with locating backups when needed.

In summary, centralizing these services would do the following:

- Reduce capital cost

- Reduce the physical footprint, often when space is at a premium (e.g., in an off-shore facility where space is limited and finite)

- Reduce power consumption and cooling demands

- Reduce maintenance demands

As noted previously, the varied application of services in automation systems (e.g., different authentication or authorization solutions) increases complexity. This creates additional security challenges.

Conduits

Conduits are the connection between two or more zones. Conduits can represent the following:

- An Ethernet-based plant network running a particular industrial protocol

- A wireless network such as ISA100, WirelessHART, or others

- An RS-232/422/485 serial link between two or more devices

Zones and Resilience

Key considerations when choosing zones are resilience and disaster response. This topic will be discussed in more detail later in this chapter, but for now it is important to consider the boundary of a zone—in particular, how the equipment within it would operate if the conduit(s) were unavailable or if the equipment in the zones at the other end of those conduit(s) was unavailable.

For example, assume network time is an essential requirement for a control system and that network time is obtained from another zone outside the physically facility. If an attack disconnects that facility from the wide area network, the control system would not operate correctly. A locally deployed NTP server, with an associated global positioning system (GPS) antenna, would overcome this failure scenario. This setup enables the control system to operate uninterrupted, in isolation. Similar considerations should be made for other equipment and the location of the DMZ itself.

The cloud has many advantages, but the loss of cloud connectivity could result in a facility shutdown. There are many real-world examples where this occurred. In one anecdotal example, a production facility depended on a printing service to produce product labels. During the WannaCry outbreak in May 2017,[87] the facility operations team was told to disconnect from the external network to prevent infection. That is when they discovered the printing service was located on the other side of the disconnected network. As a result, production halted until the connection could be restored.

Figure 5-14 is an update of the facility architecture example in Figure 5-3. This update includes a zone and conduit hierarchy, with centralized services.

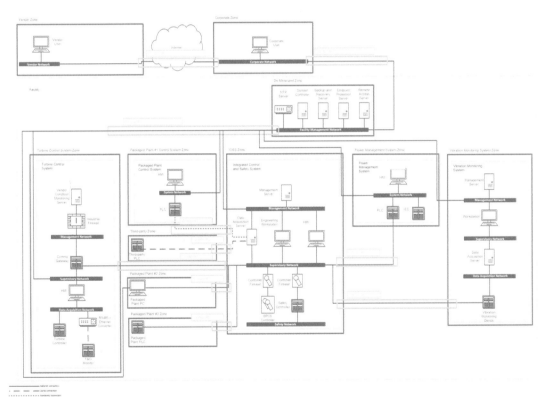

Figure 5-14. A potential zone hierarchy for the example facility architecture.

87 The WannaCry incident involved exploiting a vulnerability in Microsoft Windows and resulted in over 230,000 computers in 150 countries being infected with ransomware. Timothy B. Lee, "The WannaCry Ransomware Attack Was Temporarily Halted. But It's Not Over Yet," Vox, May 15, 2017, accessed June 21, 2021, https://www.vox.com/new-money/2017/5/15/15641196/wannacry-ransomware-windows-xp.

The architecture now includes a DMZ with network time, central domain, backup, endpoint protection, and remote access services to be shared by all the systems. Any duplicated equipment, such as NTP servers, can be removed. All traffic is directed through the DMZ avoiding direct access to any of the systems.

The management of this DMZ is critical to the successful operation of the facility. In some organizations, management of DMZ equipment may by default be the responsibility of the information technology (IT) function, with independent oversight by the operational technology (OT) function. Some organizations may create an industrial DMZ managed by the OT function with independent oversight by the IT function. As with all decisions discussed in this book, the organization must take a risk-based approach to assessing the options, ensure there are sufficient qualified resources available to administer the procedures, and apply rigorous oversight to ensure the procedures are followed and the risks are managed.

When determining conduits, all communications paths into and out of zones must be considered. These considerations include the following:

- The primary communications path for transferring data to and from the zone
    - Remote access connections
    - Cellular or other backup connections
    - Dial-up connections used by vendors
- Definitions required for each conduit identified
    - The zones it connects (to and from)
    - The communications medium it uses (e.g., Ethernet, cellular)
    - The protocols it transports (e.g., Modbus, TCP port 502)
    - Any security features required by its connected zones (e.g., encryption, multifactor authentication).

Once identified, a conduit list should be produced to capture the details. An example is shown in Table 5-2. At this stage, it is sufficient to list the names of the traffic/protocols. This list will identify and document the specific ports needed to create the firewall rules.

Table 5-2. Conduit list for example facility architecture.

Conduit ID	From	To	Traffic/Protocols
1	Vendor zone	Corporate zone	Vendor condition monitoring protocol
	Corporate zone	Vendor zone	None
2	Corporate zone	Demilitarized zone	None
	Demilitarized zone	Corporate zone	Domain control Endpoint protection (AV/patching)*
3	Turbine control system zone	Demilitarized zone	Domain control
	Packaged Plant #1 control system zone	Demilitarized zone	Endpoint protection (AV/patching)
	Packaged Plant #2 control system zone	Demilitarized zone	NTP[88]
	ICSS zone	Demilitarized zone	Remote Desktop
	Power management system zone	Demilitarized zone	Protocol
	Vibration monitoring system zone	Demilitarized zone	Backup protocol
4	Packaged Plant #1 Control System Zone	ICSS zone	Hardwired digital signal
5	Third-Party Zone	ICSS zone	Modbus server[89]
	ICSS Zone	Third-party zone	Modbus client
6	ICSS Zone	Turbine control system zone	Modbus server
	Turbine Control System Zone	ICSS zone	Modbus client
7	ICSS Zone	Packaged Plant #2 control system zone	Modbus server
	Packaged Plant #2 Control System Zone	ICSS zone	Modbus client
8	ICSS Zone	Packaged Plant #3 control system zone	Modbus server
	Packaged Plant #3 control system zone	ICSS Zone	Modbus client
9	ICSS zone	Power management system zone	EtherNet/IP server
	Power management system zone	ICSS zone	EtherNet/IP client
10	ICSS zone	Vibration monitoring system zone	Modbus server
	Vibration monitoring system zone	ICSS zone	Modbus client

*AV = antivirus

---

88 As noted earlier, to maintain resilience, a local NTP service is provided, so there is no NTP traffic required from the DMZ to the Corporate Zone.

89 This book uses the newer convention of server and client. This convention was adopted by the Modbus Organization on July 9, 2020. See https://www.modbus.org/docs/Client-ServerPR-07-2020-final.docx.pdf for further details.

With the zones and conduits identified, the next step is to segregate the zones and manage the communications across the conduits. There are several options, the most common being

- firewall,

- virtual local area network (VLAN), and

- virtual private network (VPN).

Firewall

A firewall controls access to and from a network for the purpose of protecting it and the associated devices. A firewall connects to two or more networks, creating separate network zones. A firewall operates at layer 2 or layer 3 of the OSI model—the network layer or data layer—and filters traffic by comparing network packets against a ruleset. A rule contains the following details:

- Source address

- Source port

- Destination address

- Destination port

- Protocol, TCP, User Datagram Protocol (UDP), or both

It can also include a time element (e.g., limiting remote access as needed rather than always). Most firewalls have multiple network interfaces. The firewall rule will define which interface the rule is configured on.

The firewall ruleset should be defined based on the conduit list produced earlier. For example, using the conduit list in Table 5-2, the ruleset for the turbine control system zone would be as shown in Table 5-3.[90]

The fundamental operation of a firewall is controlled by the content of the ruleset. Incorrect configuration can expose networks to unwanted threats and unauthorized access. Key points to remember when creating a firewall ruleset include the following:

- Rules that are most heavily used should be configured at the start of the list to prevent unnecessary processing.

---

90 The specific ports are shown for example only and are not intended to reflect particular products or solutions or any changes in products or solutions after this book is published.

Table 5-3. Firewall ruleset for a turbine control system zone.

From Zone	Source	To Zone	Destination	Service	Comment
DMZ	Endpoint protection server[91]	Turbine control system zone	HMI	TCP-25 TCP-53 TCP-88 TCP-135 UDP-138 TCP-389 TCP-445 TCP-464 TCP-636 TCP-3268 TCP-3269 TCP-5722 TCP-9389	Conduit 3, domain control
DMZ	Endpoint protection server	Turbine control system zone	HMI	TCP-8081 TCP-8082	Conduit 3, endpoint protection (AV)
DMZ	Endpoint protection server	Turbine control system zone	HMI	TCP-8530	Conduit 3, endpoint protection (Patching)
DMZ	NTP server	Turbine control system zone	Communications gateway	TCP-123	Conduit 3, NTP
DMZ	Remote access server	Turbine control system zone	HMI	TCP-3389	Conduit 3, remote desktop protocol
DMZ	Endpoint protection server	Turbine control system zone	HMI	TCP-9876	Conduit 3, backup protocol
ICSS Zone	Data acquisition server	Turbine control system zone	Communications gateway	TCP-502	Conduit 6, Modbus client/server

- Consider which interface the rules are configured on and whether the rules are filtering traffic as it enters the interface, inbound, or exits the interface, outbound.

- Traffic should be blocked as close to the source as possible to prevent unnecessary processing.

- "Any → Any" rules enable traffic to and from multiple sources and destinations. As a result, they require little maintenance but are extremely vulnerable. These should be avoided in all cases.

---

91 Good firewall configuration procedures require the association of unique names with IP addresses to improve the readability of a ruleset.

- Avoid creating broad, network-to-network rules. Instead, use specific host-to-host rules.

- Ensure the rules within the ruleset are arranged in the order of execution. Once a rule is detected and executed, no further rules are executed.

- Ensure the last rule is always "Deny IP Any → Any" (or the equivalent for the firewall used). It is also good practice to add the log option to this rule. This will record any traffic that reaches a rule. The log can then be analyzed for potential intrusion attempts.

- Firewalls define and group endpoints, services, and ports to be used when creating rulesets. For example, rather than creating a rule for a specific host IP address, create and associate an endpoint name.

- When a rule applies to multiple endpoints, it is easier to create a group for those endpoints and then assign the group to the rule, rather than to the individual endpoints. This makes the ruleset more legible to the administrator and therefore easier to manage.

- Ensure that all outgoing traffic is filtered. A common mistake is to apply rules to external connections coming into a network while allowing all outgoing connections. This enables an internal endpoint to establish a connection to an external compromised web server. If the original connection to an external device is filtered to limit connection to trusted destinations only, then this should not occur.

- Many applications require dynamic ports between 49152 and 65535 to be open between endpoints. Avoid opening these ports on the firewall and enforce static port configuration.

- There should be no administrative access to the firewall from any untrusted external network (e.g., telnet or secure shell). If possible, administrative access should only be allowed from within the network, preferably by physically connecting to the firewall locally. If remote administration is required, a secure communications link (e.g., VPN) should be used. This link should support multifactor authentication. That means identifying a user from their password, as well as another method such as ID card, fingerprint, or access code.

- Nonindustrial protocols should be disabled unless there is an essential business need for them. Even then, the risk should be assessed and determined to be "tolerable." Nonindustrial protocols include Simple Network Management Protocol (SMTP) for email, HTTP for web access, and Internet Control Message Protocol (ICMP), used for a variety of diagnostic services.

- Establish a review process for periodic checking of firewall logs to identify and correct any configuration issues.

- Establish a governance process for allowing requests for new services to be reviewed and approved as appropriate. The governance process should include approval by key stakeholders who understand and weigh the risk of compromise against the business benefit. The process should require that all documentation, including network diagrams, conduit lists, and the firewall ruleset, are updated accordingly.

- Over time, the requirements of a firewall may change. Systems may be retired or reconfigured. Regular reviews of the ruleset should be completed to close any ports that are open unnecessarily and remove any IP addresses no longer in use.

Standard and Industrial Firewalls

Standard firewalls can require a lot of configuration and support to be an effective security control. They are typically designed for use in climate-controlled areas, such as data centers. Their construction and environmental specification (temperature, humidity, vibration, shock, ingress protection) is not suitable for the harsh environmental conditions that exist in industrial facilities.

A specific set of firewall products exists for industrial applications. Referred to as *industrial firewalls*, these products are easy to configure and manage. They are designed and packaged with harsh conditions in mind. An example of such a product is shown in Figure 5-15. Compare the environmental specification of this product with that of a standard firewall in Table 5-4.

Figure 5-15. An example of commercially available industrial firewalls installed in a facility.

Table 5-4. Comparison of environmental specifications of standard and industrial firewalls.

Specification	Standard Firewall[92]	Industrial Firewall[93]
Operating temperature	0 to +40°C (32 to +104°F)	−40 to +70°C (°F)
Storage temperature	−35 to +40°C (−31 to +158°F)	−40 to +85°C (°F)
Humidity	20% to 90% noncondensing	10% to 90% noncondensing
Vibration	Not specified	IEC 60068-2-6: 1 g @ 20–500 Hz
Shock	Not specified	IEC 60068-2-27: 30 g for 11 ms
Ingress protection	Not specified	IP20

As well as being easier to configure, some industrial firewalls are available preconfigured to limit traffic to one or more industrial protocols (e.g., Modbus, DNP3, or EtherNet/IP). In this case no configuration is required, although this means that all commands and registers are allowed through the device. This may simplify deployment, but an accurately configured device provides better security and additional capabilities, such as monitoring and logging.

Consider the example of the turbine control system interface to the ICSS. This is Modbus/TCP based. The Modbus protocol is a simple command-response type. The server sends a command that indicates the operation (read or write, and the type of data involved). The command also identifies the range of *registers* (values) it affects. Modbus includes eight common commands, each with its own *function code*, and the *address range* identifying the function codes. Table 5-5 shows these commonly used codes.[94]

The turbine control system uses only two of these commands and a limited address range for each command. An example as shown in Table 5-6.[95]

The recommended security solution would be to deploy a configurable industrial firewall that can limit traffic to specific function codes and addresses. Then, configure the firewall so it limits function codes to Modbus 3 and 5, and the specified address ranges

---

92 FortiGate 7060E chassis. Fortinet, "FortiGate® 7000E Series FG-7060E, FG-7040E, and FG-7030E Datasheet," accessed June 28, 2021, https://www.fortinet.com/content/dam/fortinet/assets/datasheets/FortiGate_7000_Series_Bundle.pdf.

93 Tofino Argon 100 security appliance. Tofino, "Argon Security Appliance Data Sheet," DS-TSA-ARGON, Version 5.0, accessed June 28, 2021, https://www.tofinosecurity.com/sites/default/files/DS-TSA-ARGON.pdf.

94 There are additional function codes specified in the Modbus protocol. Some vendors have their own function codes for product-specific features. The commands specified here are commonly used by most systems.

95 This is an example only and does not reflect any particular vendor solution.

Table 5-5. Common Modbus commands and address ranges.

Function Code	Command	Address Range
1	Read coils	00001 to 09999
5	Write single coil	
15	Write multiple coils	
2	Read discrete inputs	10001 to 19999
4	Read input registers	30001 to 39999
3	Read multiple holding registers	40001 to 49999
6	Write single holding register	
16	Write multiple holding registers	

Table 5-6. Modbus commands and address ranges for a turbine control system interface.

Function Code	Command	Address Range
5	Write single coil ICSS commands	00001 to 00004
3	Read multiple holding registers Turbine analog values Turbine status values Process alarm set points	40001 to 40255 41000 to 41025 40801 to 40320

required. In addition, the industrial firewall should be set to log all other commands. These logs must be analyzed to identify unauthorized activity or surveillance. The arguments against this approach are poor. They include the following:

- There is uncertainty surrounding which commands and/or address ranges are required for normal operation.

- Additional work is required each time a change is made.

Figure 5-16 shows a real example, from an operational facility, where the industrial firewall was disconnected because "the automation system did not work when we connected it." There were no plans to resolve this situation before it was identified in an audit.

In an automation system like a turbine control system, there cannot be any uncertainty about commands or address ranges. Furthermore, once configured, it is unlikely that any changes will be needed.

Figure 5-17 shows the updated facility architecture with the inclusion of standard and industrial firewalls.

Figure 5-16. A disconnected industrial firewall in an operational facility.

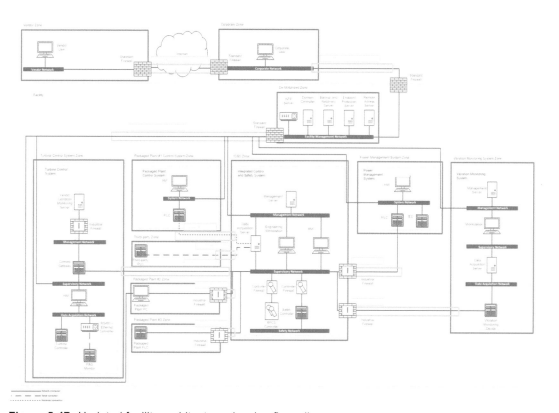

Figure 5-17. Updated facility architecture showing firewalls.

The industrial firewalls are network-based devices and may be used for more than one conduit. For instance, the firewall could be placed on the uplink of a switch that connects multiple systems. However, in this example, additional commands and/or address ranges would need to be configured. From a segregation and management perspective, it would be better to configure one industrial firewall per conduit. In this case, the firewall would be placed in line between each system and the switch. The cost per unit is marginal compared with ongoing maintenance and management. Also, this approach improves security.

The packaged plant #1 and third-party zone interfaces do not include an industrial firewall because these connections are hardwired and serial, respectively.

DMZ Firewall and Separation of Duties

Figure 5-17 shows two standard firewalls that segregate the DMZ, one from the facility zones and one from the corporate zone. It is common practice to use a single physical firewall (which can itself be configured in a redundant arrangement) with two interfaces to provide two logically separate firewalls. A better practice for automation system networks is to provide two physical firewalls and have separate teams manage them. The corporate IT team can manage the firewall that segregates the DMZ from the corporate zone. The engineering team can manage the firewall that segregates the DMZ from the facility zones. Though this arrangement may seem overly complex, it provides several security benefits:

- Different teams managing firewall rules reduces the probability of the same mistake being made in both.

- If designed correctly, the DMZ-corporate firewall can fail or be upgraded by the IT team without impacting facility operations.

- If the firewall devices are from different vendors, the same vulnerability is unlikely to be present in both devices. This reduces the probability of an exploit giving unauthorized access to a facility zone.

Virtual Local Area Network

VLANs can be used to create separate logical networks on a single physical network. This is especially useful in separating traffic related to different systems. For example, a VLAN could separate process plant closed-circuit television (CCTV) traffic from automation system traffic on the same physical network, as shown in Figure 5-18.

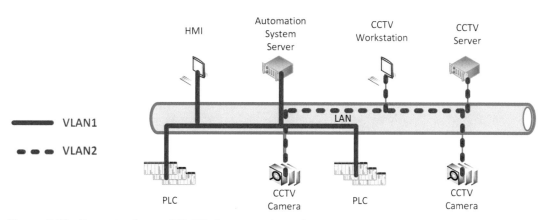

VLAN1

VLAN2

Figure 5-18. Example of use of VLANs to segregate systems.

As with firewalls, VLANs enable strict control over network traffic, in this case, limiting which devices can communicate with each other. Note, however, that as with firewalls, care must be taken to validate configurations as errors may not be obvious. Just because systems are operating normally does not mean they are secure from unauthorized operation or intrusion.

Virtual Private Network

VPNs and VLANs have many similar characteristics. Both are used to establish logical networks on top of a physical network. VPNs tend to be used to establish secure communications between geographically diverse networks. This creates a single, logical network over external physical networks such as the Internet. These secure communications are restricted to an authorized group of users. Common uses for VPNs in automation system networks include the following:

- Providing users with a secure method of remotely accessing a system to monitor and/or control equipment

- Providing vendors with a secure method of accessing condition monitoring or other maintenance-related information on their equipment

As shown in Figure 5-19:

- Remote users will authenticate to a VPN server before gaining access to the internal network. The VPN server will be installed either as part of the firewall or as a separate machine. Authorized users will have VPN software deployed on their machines to facilitate this process. For added security, deploy this VPN server in a DMZ and have remote users connect to equipment inside the network using a remote desktop application.

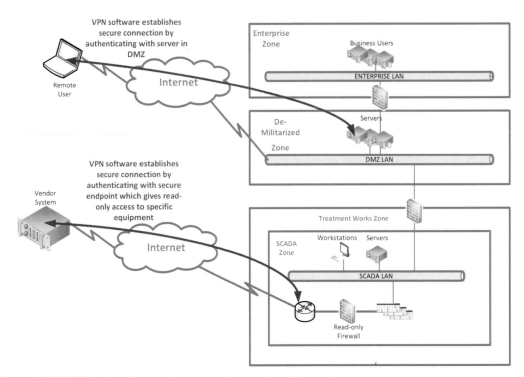

Figure 5-19. VPN setup for remote access to an automation system.

- For remote vendor access to specific equipment, the VPN connection is typically to a vendor endpoint. This device handles the VPN authentication. From there, limited access to the equipment is available through a read-only firewall. This eliminates the ability to change set points or otherwise affect the operation of the equipment.

In a VPN, the computers at each end of the tunnel encrypt the data entering the tunnel. They then decrypt the data at the other end using encryption keys. Once data is encrypted, it is impossible to read without access to the encryption keys. IP Security (IPsec) secures the storage and transmission of these encryption keys and enables secure VPNs to operate. IPsec is a set of protocols developed by the Internet Engineering Task Force (IETF) to support the secure exchange of data across the Internet. IPsec has been deployed widely to implement VPNs.

For IPsec to work, the sending and receiving devices must share a public key. This is accomplished through a protocol known as Internet Security Association and Key Management Protocol/Oakley (ISAKMP/Oakley), which allows the receiver to obtain a public key and authenticate the sender using digital certificates. Digital certificates have additional security benefits. As well as authenticating a user, they provide

- data integrity assurance, by verifying that data has not been altered in transit; and

- nonrepudiation, by proving that data was sent by a particular user, based on their certificate credentials.

There are some scenarios where asset owners approve vendors to provide technical support via VPN. This technical support may require changes to system set points or logic. In fact, the COVID-19 pandemic forced many organizations to adapt to the challenges of restricted travel and site work. In May 2020, Siemens successfully completed the start-up and adjustment of one of its gas turbines in Russia.[96] Although this case involved changes made by personnel on-site with guidance by remote experts through videoconference, there is a trend in many organizations toward performing more work remotely. This should be considered with great caution. One effective control is to limit the availability of such remote access to only when necessary, and under strict on-site supervision. Such access should be disabled by default.

System Hardening

Hardening a system means configuring equipment to reduce the likelihood of using a vulnerable program or service. Automation systems have a narrower function than IT systems. Automation systems are thus better suited to the rigorous hardening needed to prevent unauthorized access or operation.

The following hardening practices are essential for cybersecurity management of automation systems. Certain practices may not be applicable to all devices.

- **Protecting endpoints** – This includes antivirus protection and operating system patching, both of which may be performed semiautomatically or manually. In automation systems, antivirus and operating system patching should never be performed automatically. Only specific patches and antivirus definitions approved by the vendor should be deployed.[97] Machines should only be rebooted manually. This will avoid unnecessary outage of the automation system. Endpoint protection may also involve application control. Application control locks down the equipment's configuration so changes cannot be made. That means programs (malicious or otherwise) cannot be installed or executed. This

96 Fortum, "Siemens Carried Out First Remote Start-Up and Adjustment Work in Russia at Nyagan GRES," accessed June 21, 2021, https://www.fortum.com/media/2020/06/siemens-carried-out-first-remote-start-and-adjustment-work-russia-nyagan-gres.

97 This approach may lead to inconsistencies, with different vendors approving different patches or signatures, or not adequately testing against all patches before approving. Application control may provide a more consistent approach if implemented systematically.

"lockdown" approach is better suited to automation system equipment which rarely changes except for upgrades to the automation application.

- **Using USB and network port security** – USB (universal serial bus) enabled devices, such as hard drives and devices containing storage, are major sources of malicious programs. A machine should have antivirus or application control installed to prevent malicious programs from executing, but it is recommended that unused USB ports be disabled or locked. USB ports can be disabled in the machine firmware (the BIOS—basic input/output system) or the operating system. They can also be physically locked, using products such as that shown in Figure 5-20. The presence of a lock reminds users to think before plugging their device into a workstation to charge it or download personal files. A lock and key system enables an authorized user to unlock a port if needed. For additional protection, it is recommended that autorun features be disabled in Windows operating systems. This will prevent USB ports, used by mouse and keyboard devices, from intentionally or unintentionally opening USB drives and deploying malicious programs. The same approach is recommended for network ports. Ports on switches and routers should be disabled or configured to dummy VLANs that are not used. If someone connects a device to such a port, it cannot communicate. Network port locks, similar to the USB lock shown in Figure 5-20, should be installed to help change behavior and prevent users from connecting without formal approval and change control.

- **Using approved operating systems** – There are many systems in facilities today running obsolete and unsupported operating systems. These operating

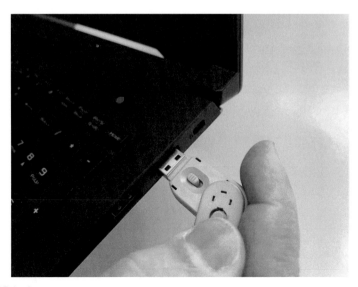

Figure 5-20. USB lock.

systems incorporate known vulnerabilities with no fixes. They may not support the deployment of endpoint protection to mitigate these risks. Obsolete operating systems stay in service because the automation system is not supported on newer operating systems, or the upgrade is considered too risky or expensive. Even in new facilities, end users may still rely on obsolete operating systems. Many automation projects are part of larger facility construction programs, which can take five years or more to complete. Designs are completed and orders placed in the early stages of the project. This lag time means the software may well be obsolete, or near obsolete, by the time the project is complete. Automation field equipment, such as operator terminals, RTUs, and communications devices, may also run operating systems that are obsolete, unsupported, or unable to support endpoint protection.

- **Disabling unused and nonessential features** – Windows operating systems come with many applications and services installed and configured by default. Good security practice is to *reduce the attack surface*, that is, reduce the scope for a cyber incident (malicious or otherwise). For example, there is no need for a web browser or email application in a Windows server used for data acquisition. Many other services are installed and running by default. In Windows 10, for instance, the print spooler is running by default. This service will not be required by the automation system. Removing programs and disabling services is important, as these are common sources of vulnerabilities. For example, the WannaCry malware exploited a vulnerability in the Server Message Block (SMB) service that runs in Windows XP by default. Many users impacted with ransomware were probably not using the SMB service. Had they disabled it, they would not have been infected. It is not only Windows devices that are affected by unused programs and services. Some RTUs and network devices incorporate features such as web servers that are not required. Again, these should be disabled to minimize the attack surface for those devices.

- **Configuring resource constraints** – Where possible, servers, workstations, RTUs, PLCs, and communications devices should be configured to limit the resources that can be consumed. For example, these devices should be restricted from installing content on a different drive or logical partition other than the operating system. Another option is to place a limit on the amount of drive space that is dedicated for uploads. Ideally, uploads should be placed on a separate drive partition to provide stronger assurance that the drive limit cannot be exceeded. This ensures log files are stored in a location that is sized appropriately. Ideally, log files should be stored on a separate drive or drive partition that is configured to allow a specific number of processes and/or network connections.

System hardening is an ongoing task. It is essential that equipment be monitored to ensure programs are not installed and services are not enabled. Likewise, only approved ports, necessary for the operation of the system, should be enabled. Lack of vigilance is a common security gap in facilities. An end user may put a lot of effort into the initial hardening of systems and equipment. Then someone is inconvenienced by a USB lock. A system service is opened, and the control is never reinstated. Gradually, the hardening erodes until it is ineffective.

Hardening Wi-Fi Networks

Wi-Fi is commonly used in automation systems. Wireless connections provide increased flexibility but present a new set of risks. Security must be carefully managed to avoid introducing these new risks to the network and the wider automation system environment. Key hardening considerations include the following:

- Ensure current encryption protocols are used. Wi-Fi encryption standards began with Wired Equivalent Privacy (WEP). This standard has been superseded by Wi-Fi Protected Access (WPA). WEP is considered insecure due to the short encryption key, only 40 bits. This enables hackers to quickly break the encryption. WPA uses 128-bit keys, and WPA-2 uses 152-bit keys. These are so time-consuming to break that they are considered secure.

- Enforce authentication on Wi-Fi networks. The Institute of Electrical and Electronic Engineers (IEEE) 802.1X standard defines authentication for Wi-Fi networks. Common Wi-Fi authentication protocols are Remote Authentication Dial in User Service (RADIUS) and Extensible Authentication Protocol (EAP). These are discussed further in the electronic access control section of this chapter.

- The service set identifier (SSID) should not be transmitted. This means that the network is not visible to those users who are scanning for available services.

- Access points should be configured to accept only devices with specific media access control (MAC) addresses. This means that devices must be approved before they can connect.

- Wireless controllers should be deployed inside a DMZ, segregated from access points.

- Dynamic Host Configuration Protocol (DHCP) automatically assigns IP addresses to devices and should be disabled. This means a device that is not connected is not assigned an IP address and must rely on a preconfigured, static address. Without an address, the device cannot communicate on the network.

As is often the case, some of these recommendations are not followed. This is especially true with the last two points. It can be inconvenient to have to make changes whenever a new device or user needs access, yet this is the type of behavior that should be enforced if a facility is to maintain its security.

Physical Access Control

Physical security of facilities is typically well understood. Most asset owners have a physical security team that assesses risks for facilities and implements a series of controls. These may include the following:

- Physical barriers or perimeters, such as walls, fences, and gates

- Security guards

- Locks and electronic ID card access

- Closed-circuit surveillance cameras

- Motion or thermal alarm systems

Automation system equipment is often located in facilities that are remote or hard to access, such as offshore oil and gas production platforms. Figure 5-21 shows a remote well facility. The automation system equipment is housed in a normally locked brick building behind a normally locked fence. Surveillance cameras are monitored 24/7. This defense-in-depth approach, with multiple controls in place, is highly recommended for the physical security of automation systems equipment. Even in physically

Figure 5-21. A remote well facility.

inaccessible facilities (e.g., offshore production platforms), automation systems equipment should be secured inside locked cabinets in buildings with restricted access. This mitigates inadvertent or accidental cybersecurity issues as well as theft or deliberate attacks.

Assuming the physical security team has put in place the elements mentioned earlier, additional considerations for physical security of automation systems equipment include the following:

- Define who should have access to each facility. This might include who has keys, or copies of keys; who is programmed into an electronic card access system; or who has the codes for keypad locks.

- Create a process for taking action when someone leaves. It is common to share codes or keys with staff and vendors. A standard process should ensure that locks or codes are changed, or card access systems are updated, when someone leaves employment.

- Enforce physical security on-site. This includes ensuring that equipment rooms (e.g., Figure 5-22) and cabinets (e.g., Figure 5-23) are locked when not in use. Visitors must always be escorted. These controls are part of the risk assessment performed by the physical security team. They are deemed necessary and should always be in place.

- Documents and storage media (e.g., CDs, USB drives) should be kept in secure cabinets on-site and should not be left unattended. Documents may contain sensitive information that can be used in conjunction with a cybersecurity attack.

Figure 5-22. An equipment room within a secured facility.

Figure 5-23. Inside an equipment room with locked cabinets.

- Cabling and equipment ports should be physically secure from interference. For example, it should not be possible to cut cables or connect equipment to networks from outside the secure perimeter.

- Equipment should be sited or protected to reduce the risks from environmental threats and hazards, as well as from unauthorized access. Figure 5-24 shows an automation system device (a laptop used to log data from a sensor array and transmit it to a control system) that is not properly secured.

- Strict procedures should be in place for bringing equipment to or removing it from a site. Authorized personnel should approve all such activities. The use of unscanned or untrusted laptops and other equipment can result in serious cybersecurity incidents. It may be necessary to prohibit all external devices and use only approved equipment when on-site.

- Incident response and disaster recovery plans should take into account all cyber, environmental, and physical risks. Exercises should be performed at the facility to ensure the plans are realistic and achievable.

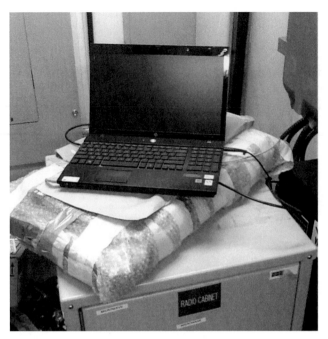

Figure 5-24. Inadequately secured automation system equipment.

Electronic Access Control

Key Electronic Access Controls

Electronic access control enables access to the resources users require, while preventing unauthorized users from gaining access to sensitive information or systems. Essential basic practices for electronic access control are as follows:

- Change all manufacturer default passwords before equipment is operational.

- Keep passwords secure. Do not share or post passwords for all to see. Figure 5-25 shows an example of bad practice: In this case, labels showing the username and password credentials are affixed to the operator workstation (bottom left of photograph).

- Change passwords regularly. Enforce password complexity so passwords are not easily cracked. In the example shown in Figure 5-25, the password had not been changed since the system was implemented. That means many people no longer with the organization still have that information.

- Update or remove access for any users who have changed their role or left the organization.

The three main elements of electronic access control are authentication, authorization, and accounting. Authentication identifies a user (e.g., username and password).

Figure 5-25. User credentials on permanent display on an operator workstation, label tape left of the keyboard

Following authentication, a user must gain authorization to perform certain tasks. Authorization determines which activities, resources, or services a user may access. Accounting measures the resources a user consumes during access. These include system time or data volumes sent and received based on logging of session statistics.

For automation systems, role-based access control (RBAC) is recommended. RBAC enables access to a resource based on a set of rules defined by a system administrator. Access properties are stored in access control lists (ACLs) associated with each resource. When a particular account or group attempts to access a resource, the operating system checks the rules contained in the ACL for that object. RBAC cannot be changed by users. All access permissions are controlled solely by the system administrator.

Windows Active Directory is an RBAC service. With Active Directory, access is managed to specific objects that fall into two categories: Resources, such as printers, and Security Principals, such as user or computer accounts and groups. The Active Directory can be viewed at several levels, called *domains*, *trees*, and *forests*.

A domain is a logical group of network objects, such as computers, users, or devices, that share the same Active Directory database. A tree is a collection of one or more domains and domain trees. The forest is the top of the Active Directory structure. A forest is a collection of trees. It represents the security boundary within which users, computers, groups, and other objects are accessible.

There are many authentication protocols, some of which will be used in automation systems:

- The Password Authentication Protocol (PAP) is one of the most basic authentication protocols. PAP transmits unencrypted passwords over networks and is therefore considered insecure. It is used as a last resort when the remote server does not support a stronger authentication protocol.

- Challenge Handshake Authentication Protocol (CHAP) is a more secure authentication protocol because it uses a coded representation of passwords.

- Kerberos is the default authentication protocol used by Windows Active Directory. This protocol relies on encryption (encryption is discussed later in this chapter) to verify the identity of devices that communicate with each other.

- OAuth is an open standard for access control used with web-based applications.

- Security Assertion Markup Language (SAML) is an XML-based standard for exchanging authentication and authorization data between parties.

- EAP is an authentication framework rather than a single protocol. EAP includes authentication protocols for dial-up, virtual private networks, and wireless.

- RADIUS is a networking protocol. RADIUS provides centralized authentication, authorization, and accounting (AAA) management for remote access users. Network access servers are the gateways that control access to a network. These servers usually contain a RADIUS client component that communicates with the RADIUS server. RADIUS is often used for 802.1X authentication as well.

These points highlight that the skills and knowledge required to administer IACS environment electronic access are significant, and the time and resources to undertake this task are is also significant. Organizations may choose to allow their IT function to administer with oversight from the OT function or have qualified personnel in the OT function administer with IT oversight.

Multifactor Authentication

Multifactor authentication is recommended for an increased level of security when performing secure activities, such as remote access. Because it is possible to compromise a username and password combination, multifactor authentication also requires one or more additional factors. The idea is that an unauthorized person is unlikely to have all the factors. Two-factor authentication is the most common. The authentication factors of a two-factor authentication scheme may include the following:

- A physical object in the possession of the user, such as a USB drive with a secret token, a bank card, or a key

- A secret known to the user, such as a username, password, or personal identification number (PIN)

- A physical characteristic of the user such as a fingerprint, an iris, or a voice

Secure Remote Access

Remote access has become a key consideration for automation systems for many reasons, including the following:

- To provide constant access to plant status regardless of geographic location

- To reduce the risk to personnel by allowing them to work at remote locations away from potentially hazardous facilities or processes

- To facilitate more flexible working arrangements for employees

There are various types of remote access in automation systems. The most common are:

- Use of an automation system application on a laptop, desktop, tablet, or smartphone to perform normal system functions from a location outside the main facilities (control room, plant)

- Access to a web-based, read-only view of automation system data, served from a system separate from the main system

- Access to PLCs, RTUs, or other devices to remotely program or monitor operation

- Vendor access to process data for equipment maintenance or service purposes

Technology, such as better communications devices and improved software, has made this objective more feasible. However, it is necessary to design remote access solutions carefully to manage both safety and security.

Remote Access Risks

Remote access for legitimate purposes opens up the same connections that would be used for unauthorized purposes. Remote access can improve efficiency and responsiveness, but it can also allow a new set of issues to arise. When providing remote access for vendors, it can be difficult to control who has access and from where. Many vendors operate globally, and agreements may not prescribe who is allowed to work on an asset owner's system and from where. Also, there may be no agreement on what background checks have been performed on these individuals. There may be no restrictions on when vendors can access systems, which systems they can access, and what they can do with that access.

The following is a list of risks to providing remote access:

- Loss of view or control of a process, or improper operation of a process (e.g., intentional operation of sewage controls) due to unauthorized malicious access

- Denial of service due to malicious deployment of malware (e.g., ransomware)

- Operational outage due to inappropriate activities conducted remotely (e.g., making changes to PLC code without on-site presence)

These risks can be mitigated by strict enforcement of remote access policies and controls. Asset owners should limit remote access as much as possible. This includes limiting who can access, what they can access, when they can access, from where they can access, and what they can do with that access.

Selecting Remote Communications Technology

Selection of technology for remote communications should be based on the following factors.

Location

Rural sites with limited cellular or broadband coverage may require an alternate solution such as satellite or radio. The following points should be considered when selecting the communications medium.

- Broadband should offer the best bandwidth but may be expensive to install, especially in remote rural areas.

- Cellular, satellite, and radio can be deployed in a wide variety of areas with minimal infrastructure, but have limitations:

  o Cellular is not currently available everywhere. The available service may not provide the required bandwidth needed for remote access connections.

- o Radio requires a line of sight to a receiver station. Although repeaters are available to extend reach, these can be cost prohibitive for a remote access solution.

- o Satellite needs only a line of sight to the sky, but bandwidth is currently limited or extremely expensive.

Availability and Redundancy

Before choosing a remote access solution, ensure the requirements/expectations are clearly defined. Remote access 24/7/365 is essential for operational management. This will require a different level of technical support than a system that is only required to supplement normal procedures on-site.

Key considerations to meet defined availability requirements are

- a service-level agreement (SLA) for remote access solution elements (hardware/software), and

- a high-availability hardware solution and/or availability of spare parts to ensure overall uptime can be met.

If the costs to provide the required SLA or high-availability solution are prohibitive, the remote access availability should be recalculated. This reduced availability must be communicated to all stakeholders. It may be necessary to introduce alternative, manual procedures if remote access availability is limited.

Depending on criticality, it may be necessary to define an alternative method to provide remote access if the primary method is not available.

Security

Security is a key aspect of remote access solutions; however, the actual security controls required vary depending on the remote access requirements. For instance, read-only access to a separate website is a lower security risk than full user access to the automation system itself.

Key security considerations for remote access solutions include the following:

- Eliminate open access to remote equipment. Connections should be made securely, for instance via a VPN.

- Incorporate encryption to prevent unauthorized interception of sensitive information, such as device usernames/passwords. A VPN should provide such features as standard.

- Adopt multifactor authentication. At the very least, access to a remote device should require a username/password (something you know) and a secure token or one-time password (something you have). Additional controls, such as biometrics (fingerprint, iris) may be required for higher-level remote access.

- There should be no direct, remote access to automation system devices. Remote access should be to the DMZ. Beyond that, additional authentication is required to access the automation system devices.

- Remote access sessions should automatically disconnect after a defined period of inactivity (e.g., 15 minutes).

- Devices supporting remote access should be strictly controlled and secured when not in use. Loss of a device should be reported immediately, and the associated account/device details removed from the system.

- Dual homed devices should not be used in remote access solutions as it is possible to bypass other segregation methods (such as firewalls) using a device that is directly connected to two separate networks.

Recommended Remote Access Policies and Procedures
The following remote access policies and procedures should be established.

User Management
- Each user should have their own user credentials (username/password).

- Remote access should be limited to essential need only.

- Remote access for vendors should be strictly limited to specific, authorized individuals.

- Vendors should not be issued a secure token or one-time password. The control room should issue a token/one-time password that enables access for each approved work activity.

- Users should be centrally managed so that access may be promptly removed if required.

- There should be automatic logging of remote access (successful and failed logins with IP addresses, usernames, passwords), allowing for review of logs as required.

- There should be a live view of remote connections accessible from the central control room. This enables connections to be terminated if required.

- Personnel changes (e.g., transfer, resignation, or termination) should trigger immediate removal of remote access accounts.

Approval Process and Oversight

- Automation systems should implement a *default deny* policy for remote access exceptions. The operational business records should document assumption of the risks before granting an exception.

- Remote access connections should be reviewed on a recurring basis (e.g., annually).

- Audit logs should be analyzed regularly (no more than weekly) and issues addressed immediately.

Technical Controls

- Remote access should be limited to devices issued by the automation system owner. This rule should extend to vendors who should use the approved devices, not those issued by their company.

- Remote access should be strictly limited to selected devices, identified by MAC address, from approved locations, identified by IP address, geofencing,[98] or via secure VPN.

- Remote access devices should be fit for purpose. Critical features such as screen size and method of data input can impact security and accuracy. A small display and touchscreen, for example, may increase the likelihood of incorrect data entry when paired with read-write access.

Procedural Controls

- All remote access activities involving changes to automation systems, or associated devices (e.g., PLC, RTU), should be only conducted under an approved permit to work. The permit should identify the planned activities, the associated risks, and any additional controls required.

- No remote access activity should be permitted if the risk of a remote-connection failure would leave the facility unsafe or in an out-of-service state.

- Remote access for particular tasks may require a specific type of connection. For instance, a cellular connection may be less reliable than a broadband connection.

- Formal, defined support schedules should be available to all involved. These document who should be connecting at any particular time.

---

98 Geofencing is the use of location-based services to locate users, and that information is used to make decisions, in this case to provide remote access. Margaret Rouse, "What Is Geo-Fencing (geofencing)?" WhatIs.com, accessed June 21, 2021.

Network Monitoring

Network monitoring is a broad term that includes

- monitoring networks for problems, such as device failures, heavy traffic, and slow response times; and

- intrusion detection and prevention.

Network monitoring tools can provide a wide range of features, including mapping of devices on a network, traffic analysis, network performance, user device tracking, and IP address management. Firewalls, servers, workstations, and other network-connected equipment produce logs that can be viewed in such tools. These logs help identify suspicious behavior, such as unauthorized attempts to access devices, and unexpected network traffic.

An intrusion detection system (IDS) monitors networks or devices for malicious activity. Networks are monitored by network-based intrusion detection systems (NIDSs). Devices are monitored by host-based intrusion detection systems (HIDSs).

An IDS uses signatures, similar to those used by antivirus software, to detect known attacks. Like antivirus tools, effective IDS protection requires regular updating of signatures, and only known attacks can be detected using these signatures. However, the IDS has a normal baseline for the network or device. It can compare current activity to this baseline and detect new, unknown attacks. In this mode of operation, false positives are more likely.

An intrusion prevention system (IPS) works with an IDS to block malicious activity when it is detected.

Network monitoring, IDS, and IPS tools are used extensively in IT networks. However, care must be taken when deploying these tools in automation system networks.

- Some tools can generate significant additional traffic. This traffic can affect the operation of automation system equipment that depends on deterministic or near-real-time responses. Passive tools that listen only to data are available to alleviate this issue.

- Often, the operation of automation systems is not well understood. The tools can produce misleading results and false positives. This creates associated inhibition of functionality.

These issues make the use of such tools in automation systems challenging. The benefits should be weighed against the following challenges:

- Many standard firewall configurations evolve over time and are not well managed. As a result, there can be obsolete rules, or rules that are incorrectly implemented. Network monitoring and IDS cannot be fully effective if firewall rules are not correct.

- In Figure 5-16, the automation system fails when the industrial firewall is connected, so the firewall remains disconnected. Network monitoring and IDS may detect unauthorized commands, but nobody will be able to recognize them if they cannot connect to the firewall.

- There are many connections and associated devices that will not be detected by network monitoring tools. Figure 5-26 shows a pair of serial devices that provide a critical operational interface.

- Even on a network, some legacy or specialist devices will not respond to or be recognized by network monitoring tools. Figure 5-27 shows an example. This device monitors vibration on rotating equipment.

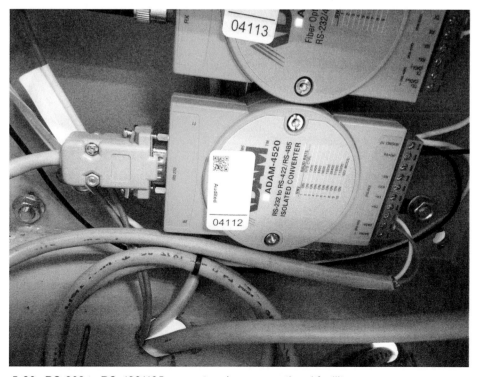

Figure 5-26. RS-232 to RS-422/485 converters in an operational facility.

Figure 5-27. Vibration monitoring rack in an operational facility.

Network monitoring, IDS, and IPS tools may have a place in automation systems, but before they are deployed it is essential that:

- The operation of all automation systems is clearly understood and documented. This includes defining all protocols, commands, and registers necessary for operation.

- Other controls are properly implemented. This includes the correct configuration and testing of all standard firewalls. It also includes industrial firewall features, such as only allowing specific commands and registers, and logging all other events.

- All equipment is properly hardened. This includes activities noted earlier in this chapter, in particular, disabling or removing unnecessary services or programs that might generate unwanted traffic.

- Procedures are in place to regularly review log files and investigate suspicious activity.

With these elements in place, it is possible that network monitoring, IDS, and IPS could be useful aids in the monitoring process.

Cybersecurity Incident Response Plan

When a cybersecurity incident occurs, an incident response (IR) plan must be initiated. Incident response plans must cover all the failure scenarios considered in the network design. The incident response plan will define

- recovery objectives;

- roles, responsibilities, and levels of authority;

- communications procedures and contact information;

- locations of emergency equipment and supplies; and

- locations of spares and tools.

The incident response plan must identify the recovery objectives for each essential function in the automation system. There are two key recovery objectives to identify:

1. **The recovery time objective (RTO)** – Defining how long the function can be out of service

2. **The recovery point objective (RPO)** – Defining how much data can be lost in the event of a failure

These objectives will dictate what must be in place, in terms of:

- SLA(s) with vendor(s)

- System design

- Spare parts, on and off-site

- What is backed up and how often

- How long the backup and restore takes, and the backup location(s)

In extreme cases, automation system unavailability may become a disaster-level situation, for instance, the loss of the primary control room in a flood or fire. This scenario requires specific recovery actions. A disaster recovery (DR) plan should be produced, defining these disaster scenarios and the required actions.

Exercising the Plans

The incident response plans and DR plan should be exercised on a periodic basis. These exercises verify that the procedures work and the documentation provides adequate detail. Varying scenarios should be chosen, and the drills should be as realistic as possible. The frequency of drills will depend on the organization. Many critical infrastructure organizations undertake these drills once or twice a year.

Near Misses

As discussed in Chapter 3, "Creating Effective Policy," cybersecurity incidents are like safety incidents in that near misses occur. These near misses are leading indicators of issues requiring attention. For example, a vendor uses its own USB drive to install software on an automation system workstation. This action may not infect the workstation, but this near miss is a failure to follow correct procedures. Not recording the near miss can lead to further procedural failures and, eventually, a cybersecurity incident. Recording the near miss should trigger a review, which may involve retraining users, issuing warnings to vendors, or other actions. The process of dealing with the near miss provides feedback on behavior to help avoid future failings.

Backup and Recovery Procedures

Backups are an essential protection for automation systems in the event of a cybersecurity incident. In an automation system, backups should be maintained for all programmable elements. The backup method, type, and frequency will vary depending on the type of equipment but will typically resemble Table 5-7.

Each equipment type should have its own procedure that describes the specific steps taken to perform the backup. Note that some automated backup may be available, either at a system level (entire system) or device level (e.g., via a PLC programming environment).

Storage and Retention

Consideration must be given to backup file storage and retention. At a minimum, files must be kept off-site to protect against a localized disaster that could destroy the equipment and backups. Depending on recovery objectives, it may also be necessary to hold

Table 5-7. Example automation system backup type and frequency.

Equipment Type	Backup Type	Backup Frequency
Server (DCS, SCADA, historian, etc.)	Disk image Application/database	On change Based on RPO (e.g., daily/weekly)
Workstation	Disk image	On change
Automation device (RTU, PLC, etc.)	Program/configuration file(s)	On change
Network device (switch, router, firewall, etc.)	Configuration file(s)	On change

copies of backups locally to allow for rapid response. In this case, backups should be kept in a fireproof safe to protect them from damage.

Backup files can be large. Transferring them over a network can be time-consuming and interfere with other network operations. It may be necessary to transfer files during quiet periods.

Backup file retention is important, but there may be limitations on available storage space. For some systems, it is common to maintain full and incremental backups. This approach minimizes the need for multiple large backup files. In such a case, there may be 1 or 2 full backups (taken monthly) and 7 to 14 incremental backups (taken daily). Other scenarios will emerge, depending on specific circumstances.

Restoration

Restore procedures describe the specific steps needed to restore the system from a backup. It is essential that these procedures be tested regularly using real backup files. Testing of this sort

- provides additional verification that the backup is completing as required, and

- verifies the restoration process.

Ideally, a setup will enable these tests to be performed without interrupting the operation of the live system. This test setup may require only one of each type of device to verify the backup/restoration process. For larger systems, the vendor may be asked to test backup file veracity using its own systems.

Other Verification Requirements

There must be some procedure to verify that malware is not present in a backup. If malware compromised a system 12 months ago, it can be assumed all backups in archive back to this time are also compromised. This may nullify all backups and require a system rebuild. Procedures should therefore include an anti-malware scan before a backup is taken, and a similar scan when restoration testing is being performed.

When backups are taken by vendors or service providers, an asset owner will need a different set of verification procedures to check that the vendor or service provider is taking the backups, testing them, and checking them for malware.

Manual Procedures

As noted in Chapter 2, "What Makes Industrial Cybersecurity Different?," policies and procedures are a critical element of good cybersecurity management. Fortunately, personnel at facilities operating automation systems are accustomed to following procedures. These environments are hazardous and following procedures can mean the difference between life and death.

As with safety procedures, cybersecurity procedures introduce inefficiencies into work processes. For example, logging in remotely using multifactor authentication and then accessing a machine via an intermediate remote access server creates several additional steps. However, as with safety, these additional steps reduce the likelihood of an incident. In Chapter 4, it was noted that administrative controls, such as procedures, are among the least effective. People inevitably find ways around the procedures. Nevertheless, procedures are an essential part of the *defense-in-depth* approach to cybersecurity management.

Key manual procedures recommended for end-user facilities are as follows:

- Require all site visitors to take a cybersecurity induction that covers the key cybersecurity rules.

- Require all personnel to complete formal training, including ongoing security awareness, and update this training annually to keep up with evolving threats, vulnerabilities, and mitigations.

- Require that all changes involve backups of equipment before and after the change.

- Require that all changes follow a formal change-control procedure that includes updating and approving all documentation.

- Require that all files are transferred using a secure, approved method.

System Availability

The terms *availability*, *reliability*, *maintainability*, and *redundancy* are often used incorrectly or interchangeably.

Availability is the probability that the system is operating properly when it is required. Availability is measured as a percentage over a defined period, for example, per day, per month, or per year. Availability over a year is the most frequently used measure for a system. An availability of 90% translates to 40 days per year downtime. An availability of 99.9999% (commonly referred to as *six nines*) translates to 30 seconds downtime in the same period. Availability is the combination of reliability and maintainability.

Reliability is a measure of the probability of a component or system to perform a required function in a specific environment for a specific period without failure.

Maintainability measures the ease with which a product can be maintained and is an essential element for successful operations.

Redundancy achieves high availability by replicating hardware so that if one device fails, another can take over. There are several types of redundant design that can be used for elements of a system:

- **Cold standby** – Although not a redundant system in the true sense, the immediate availability of spare components provides a basic level of response.

- **Warm standby** – In this scenario, duplicate components are running alongside the live equipment and can be swapped in more quickly than in the cold standby scenario. However, there is still some loss of service during the swap.

- **Hot standby** – This scenario minimizes the downtime experienced during component failure. The duplicate/standby component communicates with its live counterpart. If it detects failure, the standby component takes over. In some designs, an overall system controller monitors all components to detect failures.

The level of complexity in the redundancy design can vary considerably. Safety-critical systems may have triplicated components. Operating under a "voting" system, decisions are made based on the status of two out of the three (usually written 2oo3) components. Some systems are dual redundant but still have 2oo3 voting from three separate sets of input/output (I/O) and instruments/actuators.

The following are other measures used in system availability considerations:

- **Overall equipment effectiveness (OEE)** – Combines quality, performance, and availability to give an overall score as a percentage.

- **Service level agreement (SLA)** – A performance measure agreed upon by two or more parties for the operation of a system or service.

Specifying System Availability

Care must be taken when specifying availability for complex systems such as a DCS, which contains many elements. To properly quantify availability, users should define availability for the various functions a DCS provides, for example:

- Availability of a single operator workstation

- Availability of all operator workstations

- Availability of the historian

Each function will have its own availability target. For instance, a lower availability for the historian may be acceptable, but a high availability is needed for a single operator workstation.

Fault tree analysis is commonly used in the specification of system availability. Fault tree analysis considers each failure scenario and identifies the causes in graphical form. See the simplified "loss of view" example in Figure 5-28.

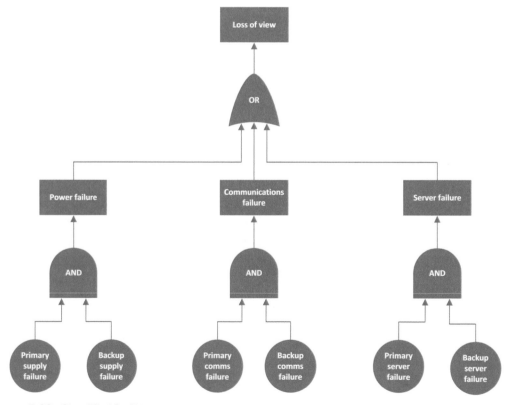

Figure 5-28. Simplified fault tree.

If the probability of the individual events (e.g., primary supply failure) are known, it is possible to calculate the overall probability of the scenario (e.g., loss of view). This probability can then be used to define availability figures for each scenario.

The fault tree method can be used to model modifications to the system design (e.g., the addition of a backup communications option) to determine the effect on availability.

Designing for System Availability

Power

Most automation system sites use an uninterruptible power supply (UPS) to ensure continuous power to equipment. The UPS monitors incoming power, detects problems, and automatically switches over to battery backup. The battery is charged continuously while the primary power supply is available. Larger sites with bigger demands require stand-alone generators (e.g., diesel) to provide backup power.

To ensure reliable power to meet system availability targets, consider the following:

- Diverse power supply options will avoid a single point of failure. Alternative options, such as solar and wind, might be more suited to remote locations where generators would be cost prohibitive.

- Power requirements depend on the criticality of each site. Certain remote sites may not require or justify the cost of a backup supply.

- Sizing of the backup supply is critical. Identify the essential elements that must be powered in the event of a primary power failure. This will determine the requirements for the backup supply. For instance, it may be acceptable to only power the PLC and several critical instruments or actuators. The cost of providing backup power for these systems will be considerably less than powering the entire facility.

- Monitoring of power supplies is essential. A failure of the primary power supply should be detected and reported via the automation system. Monitoring of backup supply options (e.g., UPS battery capacity, generator fuel capacity) makes operators aware of remaining capacity. Care must be taken when configuring alarms in automation systems related to power failure. The goal is to configure the system so that a minimum number of alarms are generated when the primary power supply fails. The operator needs only one alarm reporting a power supply failure. This configuration also applies to alarms that are generated when the power is restored and equipment is still powering up. Too many alarms reporting the same problem can be confusing and distracting to the operator.

Failure of the primary power supply should trigger a process putting the facility into a safe state before the backup power supply is engaged. This process may include some level of support from the automation system and should be captured in the relevant process control narrative.[99]

Communications Networks

There are several network topologies that can be deployed to meet various availability requirements:

- **Bus** – This is common in the PLC level of the automation system network. All devices on a bus are connected to the same cable. It is easy to implement, but if a connection is lost, then the whole network fails.

- **Ring** – Each device on the network is connected to two other devices to form a ring. This is also easy to implement, but the failure of one device will disrupt the entire network.

- **Star** – Each device has a connection to a central hub, which enables communication between all devices. This is easy to implement, and the failure of one device does not affect the other devices on the network. However, the central hub is a single point of failure and is the limiting factor in network performance and capacity.

- **Mesh** – Each device is connected to every other device on the network. This setup is much more complex and expensive to deploy but provides the most reliable device-to-device communications. In a mesh, there are multiple paths between each device pair.

- **Tree** – There is a root node and other devices connect to it. Tree networks normally have three levels of hierarchy, called *core*, *distribution*, and *access*. The hierarchy allows each level to focus on its function. For instance, the core layer is responsible for forwarding traffic between devices in the distribution layer. The hierarchical approach allows networks to be expanded while maintaining the same basic levels of performance at each layer.

---

99 A process control narrative, or PCN, is a functional statement describing how automation system components should be configured and programmed to control and monitor a particular process, process area, or facility.

Many larger networks use a combination of these topologies. Network components are then designed to meet the required availability target. Considerations include the following:

- A stacked switch combines multiple, individual switches to create a single switch. A chassis-type switch with multiple blades provides improved reliability. In this design, an individual blade can be replaced without taking the remaining blades out of service.

- Redundant firewalls can be configured to operate in active/passive mode or active/active mode. In active/passive mode, one firewall is active and processes all data while the other is in passive mode. The passive firewall is synchronized but inactive unless the primary firewall fails. In active/active mode, the processing load is shared between both firewalls. If one firewall fails, the other automatically takes on the processing for both until the failed device returns to service.

- Several protocols (e.g., Hot Standby Router Protocol, Virtual Router Redundancy Protocol) exist to allow the redundant configuration of routers.

There are numerous ways to monitor the availability of a communications network:

- The automation system can be configured to monitor key device information and report it to operators via HMI screens and alarms.

- Open-source or commercial software is available to monitor network devices using the Simple Network Management Protocol (SNMP). Some automation systems may support this protocol natively.

Servers and Workstations

Best practices for server/workstation architecture in a high-availability automation system are as follows:

- Data collection servers should be capable of operating in a hot standby arrangement, with automatic failure detection and switchover.

- Servers should be deployed at geographically diverse locations. This minimizes the likelihood of total loss of service and allows operation from various locations in the event of a disaster.

- Disk storage should be high availability, for example, a redundant array of inexpensive disks (RAID). RAID offers seven levels, 0 to 6, of progressively higher availability. The precise level of redundancy must be balanced against the additional cost, space, and power.

- Virtualization is becoming more common in automation systems and offers significant redundancy and availability benefits:

   o Virtual environments include failure detection and recovery features.

   o Virtual server instances can be taken off-line, backed up, and tested in another virtual environment.

   o Virtual server instances can be quickly deployed from a backup and redeployed in various physical locations in the event of an incident or disaster.

Embedded Devices

When designing for availability, there are several considerations for embedded devices such as PLCs or RTUs:

- **Architecture** – For most sites it will be acceptable to have a cold standby arrangement for processor units, I/O modules, and communications modules. In certain scenarios where very high availability is required, warm or hot standby architectures may be mandatory.

- **Power supply** – In hot standby architectures, a power supply shared between the redundant components can represent a single point of failure and should be avoided.

- **Data logging** – Depending on the recovery objectives, it may be necessary to log and store data in the event of equipment failure. For instance, if there is a power failure, nonvolatile data storage will ensure the data up to the power failure is not lost. It is important to understand how the automation system deals with logged data. In some systems, data is time-stamped by the PLC/RTU when it is collected. In other systems, the data is time-stamped when it is received by the automation system. In a power loss situation, the latter arrangement could result in mis-stamping of data from the PLC/RTU.

Where communications with a site is operations critical, a secondary communications link is necessary. This link should be different from, and independent of, the primary communications link. For example, if the primary communication is over a fiber network, the secondary communication could be cellular.

In sites with high-availability targets, the detection of communications failure and switchover to the secondary link must be automatic. In sites where the availability target is lower, this switchover can be manual.

Redundant functionality should be tested regularly. This may require the simulation of equipment failure. Testing must be performed under strictly controlled conditions to avoid affecting operational activities.

Support Contracts

Support contracts can have a significant impact on automation system availability. Key factors that must be in place for any support contract SLA are as follows:

- **Support hours** – Automation systems typically need 24/7/365 support; although, depending on the target availability, support may be limited to office hours.

- **Response time** – It is important to specify the skills and knowledge needed to provide support and a time window to get the right person on-site.

- **Mean time to repair** (MTTR) – This should be agreed on for all major equipment. The MTTR should be monitored and penalties levied for failure to achieve targets. This metric has a significant impact on system availability.

- **Spares** – To support the target MTTR, it may be necessary to deploy spares strategically, either on-site or at a nearby vendor location. It is essential that spares are properly maintained and accessible when needed.

Other Considerations

Internet Protocol Addressing

An IP address uniquely identifies a device on an IP network. There are two standards for IP addressing, IPv4 and IPv6. In IPv4, the address is made up of 32 binary digits, or bits, which can be divisible into a network portion and host portion. The 32 bits are broken into four octets (1 octet = 8 bits). The value in each octet ranges from 0 to 255 decimal, or 00000000 to 11111111 binary. Each octet is converted to decimal and separated by a period (dot), for example, 172.16.254.1. This is shown in Figure 5-29.

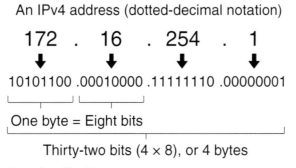

Figure 5-29. Basic structure of an IP address.

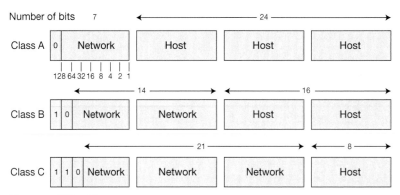

Figure 5-30. Classes of IP address.

Using IPv4 it is possible to create 4,294,967,296 (2^{32}) unique addresses. Some of these addresses are reserved. For example, addresses in the range 192.168.x.x, 172.16.x.x, and 10.x.x.x are called *nonroutable addresses* and are reserved for use on internal networks.

In the early days of the Internet, the network and host portions of the address format were created to allow for a more fine-grained network design. The first three bits of the most significant octet of an IP address were defined as the class of the address. Three classes (A, B, and C) were defined for addressing. As shown in Figure 5-30, in class A, 24 bits of host addressing allows for 16,777,216 (2^{24}) unique addresses. In class B, only 16 bits of host addressing are available, reducing the number of unique addresses to 65,536 (2^{16}). In class C, only 256 (2^{8}) unique addresses are possible because there are only 8 bits for the host address.

The class approach to network addressing proved nonscalable as the Internet grew. In 1993, the classless inter-domain routing (CIDR) method was introduced to replace it.

In IPv4, the CIDR notation is written as the first address of a given network followed by the bit-length of the network portion of the address. For example, 192.168.1.0/24 means that there is an address range that starts at 192.168.1.0 and has 256 unique addresses up to 192.168.1.255 (the /24 signifies that the network portion of the address is 24 bits, leaving 8 bits for the host address, which yields 2^{8} or 256 addresses).

In 2015, all 16,777,216 externally routable IPv4 addresses were allocated, leaving nothing available for future use. Anticipating this issue, plans to replace the standard were developed. IPv6 is the current address standard for the Internet, although IPv4 addressing continues to be supported in parallel and will be for the foreseeable future. All new network equipment must support IPv6.

IPv6 uses a 128-bit address that allows 2^{128}, or approximately 3.4×1038, addresses. The CIDR notation for IPv6 addresses is similar to that for IPv4 addresses. For example, the

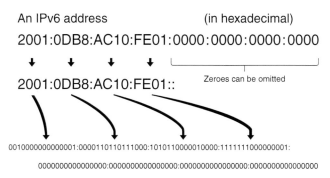

Figure 5-31. The IPv6 address format.

IPv6 address 2001:db8::/32 denotes an address block starting at 2001:0db8:0000:0000:0 000:0000:0000:0000 with 296 addresses (having a 32-bit routing prefix denoted by /32 leaving 96 bits for host addresses). This is shown in Figure 5-31.

Most automation system equipment still uses IPv4 addressing. Automation systems are not intended to be Internet facing and do not need to use the IPv6 scheme. However, given the longevity of automation system equipment, it is highly recommended that end users ensure equipment is IPv6 compatible, even if this functionality is not used initially.

In automation systems implementations, IPv4 schemes have issues worth noting.

- Many vendors have their own preferred IP addressing schemes. This can include the allocation of large blocks of address ranges that are then no longer available for use in the wider network. In one case, an automation system vendor insisted on allocating the network 10.0.0.0/8 to one of its networks. This equates to 16 million unique addresses. This made it easy for the vendor to allocate addresses to new devices as needed. Unfortunately, this meant the end user was unable to access the 10.0.0.0 network range for other devices in their facility and was forced to change to a different scheme. This issue was not addressed in early requirements specification or contract phases.

- Some systems still use host files[100] for the reconciliation of host name and IP address. This is usually due to legacy factors, in particular the implementation of automation systems without full IT network features, such as DNS. It is not a good practice. Changes would require administrative file access to the relevant machines, which might be compromised by unauthorized users.

---

100 A host file is a clear text file stored on a server or workstation that contains a list of hostnames and associated IP addresses. This is a simplified, but decentralized, version of DNS where network devices share and update a similar list in real time.

When implementing a facility-level network, it is essential that an IP address scheme is defined early and included in requirements with vendors. Requirements should also specify that obsolete methods, such as the use of host files, are not allowed.

Encryption

Encryption transforms data so that it is unreadable. Even if someone gains access to the data, they cannot read it unless they decrypt it. The data to be encrypted, also called *plaintext* or *cleartext*, is transformed using an encryption key. The encryption key is a value that is combined with the original data to create the encrypted data, also called *ciphertext*. The same encryption key is used at the receiving end to decrypt the ciphertext and obtain the original cleartext.

In addition to ensuring data is not read by the wrong people, encryption protects data from being altered in transit and verifies the sender's identity.

There are three main options for encrypting data:

- Symmetric, or private-key, encryption

- Asymmetric, or public-key, encryption

- Hybrid encryption

In symmetric encryption, the key used to encrypt and decrypt the message must remain secure, which explains the alternate name *private-key encryption*. Anyone with access to the encryption key can decrypt the data. Using symmetric encryption, a sender encrypts the data with the key, sends the data, and the receiver uses the same key to decrypt the data. This is shown in Figure 5-32.

Asymmetric encryption uses two keys, one for encryption and one for decryption. This is shown in Figure 5-33. The encryption key is known as the *public key*. It is freely

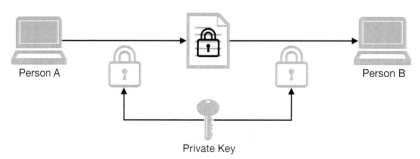

Figure 5-32. Symmetric encryption.

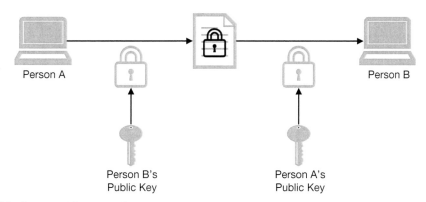

Figure 5-33. Asymmetric encryption.

available to everyone to encrypt messages. This is why asymmetric encryption is also known as *public-key encryption*.

Asymmetric key systems ensure a high security level, but their complexity makes them slower and computationally more demanding than symmetric key encryptions. Hybrid encryption systems use symmetric and asymmetric systems, combining the advantages of the two. Hybrid systems have the safety of the public key and the speed of the symmetric key.

In the hybrid system, a public key is used to safely share the symmetric encryption system's private key. The actual message is then encrypted using that key and sent to the recipient.

Another unique form of encryption, known as *hashing*, is commonly used to protect sensitive data. In hashing, an encrypted version of data (the hash) is created but cannot be decrypted. An example of hashing is shown in Figure 5-34. Hashing is often used to securely store passwords. In this scenario, to verify a password, a hash is created on the fly and compared against the stored hash. This avoids the need to store and

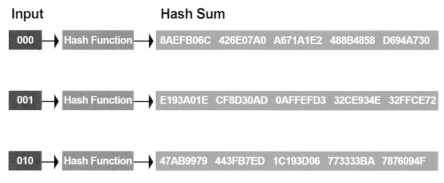

Figure 5-34. Hashing.

transmit the unencrypted version of the password, which could be accessed by unauthorized users.

There are two possible applications of encryption in automation systems:

1. **Protecting data at rest** – Such as protecting passwords stored on workstations or servers or personnel data stored in databases. This is typically achieved using hashing or private-key encryption. It is not typically necessary to encrypt process data at rest. However, organizations should perform a risk assessment to determine the sensitivity of data, including process data.

2. **Protecting data in transit** – Such as protecting passwords transmitted from workstation to server during the authentication process or preventing unauthorized commands from being executed. VPNs and secure web communications (HTTPS are examples of encryption used to protect data in transit. Some automation protocols, notably DNP3, now support encryption. As with process data at rest, it is not typically necessary to encrypt process data in transit, although each organization should determine its own requirements.

ISASecure

The ISA Security Compliance Institute (ISCI) is a nonprofit organization that has developed several product certification programs for IACSs and the components of these systems.[101] These programs are based on certification around the ISA/IEC 62443 Series, *Security for Industrial Automation and Control Systems*.

The current ISASecure certification programs are listed below.

- Security Development Lifecycle Assurance (SDLA), which certifies that the security development life cycle of a vendor meets the requirements in ANSI/ISA-62443-4-1, *Product Security Development Life-Cycle Requirements*.

- System Security Assurance (SSA), which certifies that IACS products have the capability to meet the requirements in ANSI/ISA-62443-3-3, *System Security Requirements and Security Levels*, and have been developed in accordance with an SDLA program compliant with ANSI/ISA-62443-4-1-2018, *Security for Industrial Automation and Control Systems – Part 4-1: Secure Product Development*

---

101 See https://www.isasecure.org/en-US/About-Us for more details.

Lifecycle Requirements (formerly Part 4-1: *Product Security Development Life-Cycle Requirements*).

- Component Security Assurance (CSA), which certifies that IACS component products have the capability to meet the requirements in ANSI/ISA-62443-4-2-2018, *Security for Industrial Automation and Control Systems – Part 4-2: Technical Security Requirements for IACS components*, and have been developed in accordance with an SDLA program compliant with ANSI/ISA-62443-4-1-2018, *Security for Industrial Automation and Control Systems – Part 4-1: Secure Product Development Lifecycle Requirements* (formerly Part 4-1: *Product Security Development Life-Cycle Requirements*). Certified component products can be embedded devices, such as controllers; host devices, such as PC workstations; network devices, such as firewalls; and software applications.

Certification is conducted by ISO 17065 accredited certification bodies (CBs). A certificate is issued that shows details of the product, including relevant release numbers, the version of the standard referenced, and the date of certification. An example certificate is shown in Figure 5-35.

Although many vendors have SDLA, SSA, and CSA certification, at the time of this writing, it is still not common for asset owners to demand certified vendors, systems, or components. As noted at the beginning of this chapter, there are substantial benefits to building facilities around certified vendors and products, just as there are with hazardous-area certified equipment.

- Products that are *secure by design*, developed by vendors who are certified to follow standards for their processes and procedures, form a much better foundation for a secure facility.

- The onus is on vendors, rather than asset owners, to obtain and maintain third-party certification for their products. The asset owner can save time and money by avoiding the need to perform audits of vendors and their products.

- To be compliant, the vendor must provide clear instruction to the asset owner on secure deployment of the product. This will save additional time and money for the asset owner, who will not need to develop security requirements. It also provides a greater degree of consistency that is easier to maintain.

The main driver for vendors to obtain certification is market pressure. Few vendors will take the initiative to invest in certification without a business case for a return on that investment. Unfortunately, many asset owners still do not fully understand automation

The manufacturer
may use the marks:

Certified Device
ISASecure

CERTIFIED
IEC 62443
exida
SL-C 1

Certification Report:
ABB 800M Q2003111 CSA
1.0.0 ISASecure Device
Assessment Report V1R1

Application Restrictions:
The unit shall be operated in a network and
operational environment meeting the
assumptions in the product certification
report.

Validity:
Product certificate remains valid under
conditions:
- The following SDLA certificate
  remains valid: ISASecure® SDLA
  certificate number ABB 2003111 C001
  issued to ABB AB
- AC 800M / AC 800M HI
  Controller V6.1.x remains under
  security management practices
  thereby certified

Revision 1.0 May 20, 2021

ANAB
ANSI National Accreditation Board
A C C R E D I T E D
ISO/IEC 17065
PRODUCT CERTIFICATION
BODY
#1004

ISASecure Chartered Laboratory:
exida
80 North Main St.
Sellersville, PA 18960
License: ISCI-CL0001
ACLASS Cert No: AT-1531

exida®

T-XXX V1R0

Certificate / Certificat

Zertifikat / 合格証

ABB 2003111 C001

exida hereby confirms that the

AC 800M / AC 800M HI Controller

ABB AB

Malmö/Västerås, Sweden

Has been assessed per the relevant requirements of:

ANSI/ISA-62443-4-1:2018, IEC 62443-4-1:2018 Secure product development lifecycle requirements

ANSI/ISA-62443-4-2:2018, IEC 62443-4-2:2019 Technical security requirements for IACS components

ISASecure Component Security Assurance (CSA) 1.0.0 Capability Security Level 1 requirements for embedded devices, referencing errata CSA-102 v1.0

The normative documents and issue dates that define this certification are listed at www.isasecure.org

Assessment	Subject under Assessment	Date	Current releases at time of assessment
ISASecure® CSA evaluation	AC 800M Controller Models PM857(HI), PM858(PA), PM862(PA), PM863(HI), PM866A(PA), PM867(HI) V6.1.x (x greater than 0)	May 20, 2021	6.1.1-0

Evaluating Assessor

Certifying Assessor

Figure 5-35. Example ISASecure certificate.

Source: *International Society of Automation, ISASecure website. https://www.isasecure.org/en-US/ End-Users/IEC-62443-4-2-Certified-Components.*

systems security. Many security questionnaires in requests for proposal include questions oriented entirely around information security, such as the following:[102]

- Are you certified and/or audited to any information security or quality standards such as ISO/IEC 27001, ISO 9001, SAS 70, or PCI DSS?

---

102 These questions are similar to a sample from a real questionnaire from an asset owner. Identifying details have been removed where applicable.

- Will any <asset owner> information be stored, processed, or accessed from outside of <country>?

- What security controls are in place to keep <asset owner> systems and data separate from other client data?

- Will access to <asset owner> information held on your systems be able to be gained via a remote connection?

These questions are important, but without asking for ISA/IEC 62443 certification or any details of automation systems-related controls, there is no requirement for vendors to learn about or pursue them.

When asset owners finally demand certified automation system vendors and products, the business case will be clear and vendors will comply. This compliance will greatly improve the inherent security of automation systems products.

Summary

Despite the general awareness of cybersecurity risks, many asset owners and vendors are still not providing or maintaining secure automation systems. Although some automation vendors have begun developing their own secure architectures, and some have obtained third-party certification, there is still much to be done.

Asset owners that are security-aware have developed their own internal automation systems security standards. They have been designing and reviewing solutions from vendors. The lack of consistency of approach, even within asset-owner organizations, introduces additional cost while failing to achieve the most secure outcome.

Standardization is essential if asset owners are to improve their cybersecurity posture and reduce the cost of deployment. Asset owners should focus on ensuring the essential elements of standardized designs are in place before looking at other, more advanced controls.

A secure network design is a foundation of good cybersecurity posture. Many implementations fail at this stage due to a lack of understanding of secure design principles. Among these is the use of the Purdue hierarchy. It can define a functional design that can be converted into a physical one, with all the necessary security zones and conduits in place.

The demand for IIoT and cloud solutions is driving poor network design. These solutions may work, but without the resilience needed by most asset-owning businesses. Unfortunately, many discover this lack of resilience during an incident.

Even with a secure network design, it is critical that equipment be properly hardened. Physical and electronic access control must be put in place, with robust manual procedures, before advanced solutions like network monitoring or intrusion detection are deployed.

Even with the most secure solution feasible, an asset owner will still experience cyber incidents. Being prepared for these, with proven tested incident response and disaster recovery plans, supported by backup and recovery processes, will make the difference between a minor and major outage or incident.

Certification of vendors and products is a key means to raise the standard of automation systems security. Hazardous-area certification became a business requirement because of safety concerns. The link between cybersecurity and safety should be clear to all asset owners, as described in Chapter 4. Once cybersecurity certification for automation systems becomes the norm, asset owners will be able to implement more secure facilities at a fraction of the current cost.

6

Pitfalls of Project Delivery

Introduction

Most cybersecurity literature and training reference the challenge of applying cyber-security controls to legacy equipment. Typical of these references are "There is a large installed base of SCADA [supervisory control and data acquisition] systems, ranging from current levels of technology back to technologies from the 1980s (and possibly older),"[103] and "In the long run, however, there will need to be basic changes in the design and construction of SCADA systems (including the remote terminal units—RTUs) if they are to be made intrinsically secure."[104]

One might think that a project involving a new facility, or an upgrade to an existing facility, would present the ideal opportunity to resolve this challenge. Unfortunately, this is not the case. Despite the widespread awareness of the cybersecurity threat and the availability of standards, certified products, certified professionals, and collective experience, systems are being deployed that lack the most basic security controls. In addition, the projects themselves create additional security vulnerabilities due to poor training, awareness, and oversight among personnel. In addition, a focus on efficiency and cost reduction means that many of the duties involved in managing cybersecurity are added to existing workloads, rather than to dedicated professionals with the right mix of skills and knowledge.

---

103 William T. Shaw, *Cybersecurity for SCADA Systems* (Tulsa, OK: PennWell Corporation, 2006), 389.
104 Shaw, *Cybersecurity for SCADA Systems*, 390.

The key factors required to correct these issues are

- secure senior project leadership support,

- embed cybersecurity throughout the project,

- embed cybersecurity requirements in all contracts,

- raise awareness within the project team, and

- implement rigorous oversight processes.

Good cybersecurity requires significant investment, often without an obvious financial return. Like any essential element, cutting costs in cybersecurity creates additional expenses down the line. These additional costs may crop up later in the project or during the operational phase.

Secure Senior Project Leadership Support

Operational technology (OT) projects typically involve large construction elements, such as a new oil and gas platform, manufacturing plant, or water/wastewater facility (such as that shown in Figure 6-1). These projects fall into two broad categories, greenfield or brownfield. A greenfield project involves all new construction, whereas a brownfield project may expand an existing plant (e.g., to add more production capacity), modify a process (e.g., to change a wastewater treatment process to a more efficient format), or upgrade some elements of the process (e.g., replace obsolete equipment).

Figure 6-1. A typical water/wastewater construction project.

As noted in Chapter 2, "What Makes Industrial Cybersecurity Different?," a typical OT project has a different focus than a typical information technology (IT) project. An IT project is focused on technology (software and hardware). As a result, the security element is usually better understood by the project team. An OT project is typically focused on the physical plant and its construction. Even in a brownfield project, the costs for the modifications to the facility are likely to far outweigh the costs for the modifications to the technology. In another sign of the significance of technology modifications, upgrades to obsolete OT systems tend to be added to facility outages rather than having their own dedicated outages.

Technology, including automation systems, is a small part of any capital expenditure project budget. Cybersecurity management of the technology is an even smaller subset of that technology budget. The importance of cybersecurity may not be reflected in the budget but ignoring its importance can have broad implications. Without support for cybersecurity integration from senior project leadership, numerous opportunities will be missed, namely:

- Incorporating cybersecurity as a core project activity

- Ensuring cybersecurity requirements are embedded in all contracts

- Raising awareness of cybersecurity within the project team

- Implementing rigorous oversight processes

Asset owners with a strong cybersecurity posture will have adopted standards or policies that dictate how projects deliver secure solutions. However, even with this level of control, it is possible that cybersecurity management could be more effective.

One key factor is project execution. Large infrastructure projects use a form of contract called *engineering, procurement, and construction* (EPC). This contract is between an asset owner and a contractor. Well-known EPC contractors include Bechtel, Black & Veatch, Burns & McDonnell, Fluor, McDermott, Saipem, Worley, and Wood. EPC contracts are referred to as *turnkey* because the contractor provides a complete facility for the asset owner who only needs to turn a key to start it up.

Because EPC contracts cover the entirety of the project life cycle and the delivery of the entire project scope, responsibility for cybersecurity design and governance should be explicitly included. Unfortunately, at the time of this writing, EPC contracts typically do not identify cybersecurity as a major element. This is largely due to the small financial value involved. This oversight can result in a lack of ownership of issues during the project and creates the potential for gaps in the final deliverables.

Chapter 3, "Creating Effective Policy," noted that proper cybersecurity governance requires, among other things, senior management representation and clear ownership. A critical element of a successful project is a member of the senior project leadership with responsibility for cybersecurity. This responsibility must include a clear definition of the goals, and authorization by the rest of the leadership to take the necessary action to achieve these goals.

Given the contractual relationship, it is essential that this senior project leadership include the asset owner and the EPC contractor. With this ownership in place and visible to the senior project leadership, it is possible to address the other factors.

Embed Cybersecurity Throughout the Project

Cybersecurity is often addressed too late in a project. Cybersecurity must be considered throughout every stage. Failing to acknowledge cybersecurity at the outset will result in costly rework. Not only is this approach more expensive, but it also creates a solution that is ultimately less secure. Recall the comparison to hazardous-area equipment in Chapter 4, "Measure to Manage Cybersecurity Risk." Although it is possible to use explosion-proof enclosures to protect equipment, it is much safer to design a system that is not capable of causing an explosion in the first place.

The equivalent situation for cybersecurity is equipment provided with little or no thought for mitigating vulnerabilities. This leaves asset owners to address those vulnerabilities themselves, using less effective solutions. For example, a control system vendor may provide Windows-based human-machine interfaces (HMIs) that sit on an isolated network with no means to deploy operating system patches other than by manual means. If this vulnerability is not identified and addressed early in the design, the asset owner will be left to determine an alternate means of applying these patches. This alternate solution will involve less effective, manual methods and create new risks, such as the use of removable media. The operations team may not have budgeted time to perform this complex task. As a result, the equipment will fall out of date, exposing a security vulnerability to accidental or deliberate exploitation. Such an incident could range from a minor production outage to a catastrophic accident, all because the contractor failed to properly incorporate cybersecurity into the project.

Table 6-1 shows the typical EPC project stages together with key cybersecurity considerations for each stage.

Feasibility

As previously noted in Chapter 2, EPC projects tend to run for many years. For the systems and networks being implemented, cybersecurity is more than a design or

Table 6-1. Project stages and key cybersecurity considerations.

Stage	Key Cybersecurity Considerations
Feasibility	Cybersecurity risks in each phase of the project Cybersecurity risks in the final facility
Conceptual engineering	Cybersecurity risk comparison for high-level logical design options
Preliminary engineering[105]	Cybersecurity requirements for systems or devices Verification requirements
Detailed engineering	Contractual requirements and payment milestones Detailed test specifications Cybersecurity design reviews
Construction	Management of change Incident response preparedness
Commissioning	Management of change Incident response preparedness Red-team assessment
Start-up	Management of change Incident response preparedness
Handover and closeout	As-built documentation Asset inventory

assurance issue. During the feasibility stage, the project team should consider the risks related to each subsequent phase of the project. This includes the time to deploy controls, procedural or technical, to manage these risks. Establishing a solid foundation of good governance, as part of a comprehensive cybersecurity management system, will reduce delays to a project. Putting this system in place early may prevent a cybersecurity incident or last-minute technical issues.

Consider the December 2018 Shamoon 3 cyberattack that targeted service providers in the Middle East. EPC contractor Saipem suffered significant disruption at locations in the Middle East, India, Aberdeen, and Italy. According to a Reuters report, up to 400 servers and 100 workstations were crippled by the attack.[106] The impact was not limited to Saipem. Its customers all over the world suffered disruption to their projects as they were forced to take action to prevent being drawn into the attack. Such actions included disabling user accounts and removing access to systems. These preventive measures forced projects to find workarounds until the incident was satisfactorily addressed. These workarounds can introduce new security vulnerabilities that require additional attention to avoid increasing exposure to attack. Saipem customers

---

105 Also called front-end engineering design, or FEED.
106 Stephen Jewkes and Jim Finkle, "Saipem Says Shamoon Variant Crippled Hundreds of Computers," Reuters, December 12, 2018, accessed June 21, 2021, https://www.reuters.com/article/us-cyber-shamoon/saipem-says-shamoon-variant-crippled-hundreds-of-computers-idUSKBN1OB2FA.

invested significant time and effort investigating the incident to determine their exposure. Sensitive information may have been exfiltrated, and accounts may have been compromised. This weeks-long investigation distracted employees and drew down resources needed for the actual EPC project.

If Saipem and its customers recognized this risk during the early stages of the project, they could have developed defenses such as awareness training, monitoring, and joint incident response plans. Although these mitigations may not have prevented the attack, they would have reduced the impact to the project.

Engineering

The engineering phase of the project focuses heavily on the design of construction elements, for example, the fabrication of a vessel or oil and gas platform, or the construction of a treatment plant.

During this phase, automation system vendors refine the details of their solution in several ways:

- Defining the list of data, including the instrument type, location, and data type

- Defining the control strategy

- Conducting or contributing to hazard and operability studies (HAZOP), including a control system HAZOP (CHAZOP) that focuses specifically on failures of the control system

- Identifying interfaces with other systems

- Designing the physical network arrangement

- Designing the cabinet arrangement and cabling details

Decisions made in the engineering phase can have significant impacts later in the project or during operations. For example, there is a misconception that isolating automation system equipment from other networks addresses cybersecurity threats to that system. Obviously, this is not the case. Isolated systems are exposed to many cybersecurity threats, including the use of uncontrolled removable media. Furthermore, the isolation of automation systems creates operational challenges that reduce cybersecurity posture. For example, operating system patches and antimalware updates must be transferred manually using removable media, rather than through secure network-based mechanisms. As discussed, manual processes are vulnerable to failure.

Therefore, cybersecurity should be treated as a key design consideration during the engineering phase. Issues that must be considered are as follows:

- **Updating equipment with patches during operation** – This must include consideration of how vendor-approved patches can be delivered to the equipment and how they can be applied with minimal operational disruption.

- **Maintaining anti-malware protection** – This may involve the use of application control, or antivirus software. In either case, the vendor will advise on configuring the equipment to work with the protection.

- **Maintaining, testing, and restoring backups** – Automation systems do not typically need frequent backups. Still, backups of machines must be available in the event of a disaster situation. A proven process for restoring these backups is also needed. A failure to consider a practical means for storing and retrieving backups, or a failure to practice the process, can result in extended periods of downtime.

- **Managing user access** – Many automation systems have elementary access control features such as simple Windows Workgroup accounts. In many cases, these accounts are shared between users. A facility with multiple automation systems is difficult to manage effectively. Periodically changing passwords, and updating user accounts for joiners, movers, and leavers will involve manual processes vulnerable to failure.

- **Managing remote access** – Many automation system vendors require some level of remote access. This access might provide a data stream from the system to allow condition monitoring or to allow remote diagnosis during failure situations. Many projects only address this requirement in the operations phase. That is when the facility is added to the vendor's support agreement with the asset owner. At that point, there is likely no physical space to house the necessary equipment, nor cabling in place to enable the remote access. As a result, compromises are made. Equipment is stored where space allows, rather than where it should be located. Cables are run to accommodate this equipment, bypassing the necessary segregation controls that were put in place for the rest of the network. Remote access requirements are discussed further in Chapter 5, "Standardized Design and Vendor Certification."

A common failure during project design is not standardizing on shared resources. This is discussed in detail in Chapter 5. Automation system vendors may have their own solutions for backup, patch management, anti-malware, and user access. However, in a facility with multiple vendor systems, the asset owner should define these features and require the vendors to use them. Otherwise, the asset owner must manage multiple solutions during the operations phase.

Construction

There are two major issues relating to cybersecurity during the construction phase of a project:

1. Management of change

2. Incident response preparedness

Management of Change

Despite the best efforts of everyone involved in the engineering phase, errors and omissions will occur that must be corrected. A typical example is the need to run additional cables to accommodate system connections.

Often, some requirements are omitted during the project phase. For instance, equipment required for vendor remote access to its system may not be included in the project scope because it is considered part of a separate maintenance contract. As a result, changes may be needed to accommodate this equipment later, as well as additional cabling to provide connectivity.

Changes may not involve omissions related to known requirements. Due to the long-term nature of the project, new requirements may arise. For example, the asset owner may incorporate new equipment to support additional production capacity.

In all these cases, a rigorous change-management process should be established to address the impact and procedure for these changes. The impacts may include the effect on project timescale and cost. The process may also address such issues as performance and resilience.

Cybersecurity must be included in the management of change process, to ensure that:

- Drawings and other documents are reviewed and updated when making changes. Accurate drawings and documents are essential to successfully manage cybersecurity. The failure to indicate the connectivity of equipment, for instance, can lead to an incorrect assessment of product vulnerability.

- All procedural cybersecurity controls, such as multifactor authentication and anti-malware checks, are followed when executing the change.

- All technical controls are in place on completion of the change. For example, an industrial firewall may be disconnected during testing to resolve a system-to-system communications failure. This firewall must be reinstated once the issue is resolved to ensure all necessary controls are properly deployed. See Figure 5-16 and the associated commentary in Chapter 5 for a real example of this scenario.

Incident Response Preparedness

Figure 6-2 shows a typical EPC project construction site. There may be dozens, or even hundreds, of workers operating around technology that is vulnerable to cybersecurity incidents. Even if they are not working on the technology itself, personnel will need access to communications networks to collaborate, report, and work safely. This may take the form of a temporary wireless network with Internet access. Internet access may encourage workers to check their email or browse social media. If these workers are not aware of cybersecurity risks, their devices or the network itself could be compromised. Even if the impact is limited to worker devices and the temporary network, this disruption could delay the project.

While facility construction is underway, the automation system vendors will be working on their systems. This work may take place in the vendor's facilities, or they may rent a large warehouse such as that shown in Figure 6-3.

For the automation vendors, this phase of the project can last well over 12 months. During this time, numerous individuals from the asset owner, EPC contractor, and the automation system vendor will come into contact with the automation system equipment.

Figure 6-2. Workers at a typical EPC project construction site.

Figure 6-3. Typical automation vendor development facility.

Basic cyber hygiene tasks, such as anti-malware protection, backup, and electronic access management, should be performed during the construction phase, but this is not always the case. This negligence can be attributed to poor cybersecurity awareness, limited oversight, and minimal contractual obligations. Many automation system vendors assume that because the equipment is not operational, these tasks are not necessary. These important steps are often seen as time-consuming and overly cautious for equipment that is still under development. However, the risk to the project timescale and associated cost of neglecting basic cyber hygiene is significant. For example:

- A failure to maintain regular backups could result in a loss of several days, or even weeks, of progress in the event of a cybersecurity incident.

- A failure to maintain rigorous electronic access control, especially with respect to joiners, movers, and leavers, can lead to a compromise of systems.

- As with operational automation systems, there is a misunderstanding that because these systems are not usually directly connected to the Internet, they are not at risk from external threats. These systems are often indirectly connected to the Internet,[107] for example, through a connection to the office network

---

107 According to a 2019 Dragos report, 66% of incident response cases involved adversaries directly accessing the Industrial Control System (ICS) network from the Internet. Dragos, "2019 Year in Review," accessed June 21, 2021, https://www.dragos.com/wp-content/uploads/Lessons_Learned_from_the_Front_Lines_of_ICS_Cybersecurity.pdf.

allowing developers to work from their desks. When the automation system vendor is operating from a temporary facility, there is an even greater chance of indirect connectivity through poorly managed temporary firewalls.

- Even with no connection to the Internet, there is a major risk that systems could be compromised from within. This is especially true with poor management of removable media. This risk is increased when secure file transfer facilities are not provided. Developers will need a secure means to transfer files to and from servers and workstations on the automation system.

The COVID-19 pandemic necessitated a major change in work habits beginning in 2020. For example, remote access to systems under development was essential to avoid significant project delays due to travel restrictions. The longer these remote activities are in place, the more likely they are to continue beyond the pandemic. While convenient, increased remote access means increased cybersecurity risk during project execution. This is true if the remote access solution is not developed with security in mind.

To prevent an incident during this phase, a shared cybersecurity incident response plan must be in place and regularly tested. This response plan should address the following:

- The scope of the plan—specifically, which systems, locations, circumstances, situations, and teams are included/excluded

- A prioritized list of possible incidents

- The organizational structure for the incident response team that clearly defines roles, responsibilities, and levels of authority

- Communications procedures and contact information

- Reporting procedures and associated forms

The plan must identify incident handling procedures and categorize these procedures for four stages:

1. **Before the incident occurs** – What activities must take place to be prepared for an incident? One example is regular backup of systems.

2. **While the incident is underway** – What activities must be performed in response to each type of incident? An example would be verifying the details of malware on detection.

3. **Immediately after the incident** – What activities should take place when the incident is defined as over? These might include communications to various stakeholders, damage assessment, and restoration of any services that were suspended during the incident.

4. **During recovery** – Which activities must take place once the incident is over? Examples include replacing damaged equipment and conducting a lessons-learned exercise or root-cause analysis.

As noted in Chapter 3, there should be a culture of reporting incidents, including near misses. This reporting should be used by the project governance structure to introduce improvements.

Commissioning

Typical Challenges during Commissioning

In a complex, multiyear project, delays are all but certain. The commissioning team will be under pressure to complete their task and make up lost time where possible.

To get the project back on schedule, the commissioning team will eliminate any nonessential work. Cybersecurity is often on that list. The management of change process, discussed during the construction phase, will prevent these risky shortcuts. Cutting corners on cybersecurity during commission could include the following:

- Failure to update and review drawings or other documents when making changes required to complete commissioning tests

- Avoiding some cybersecurity controls to save time, such as disabling multifactor authentication, deferring critical software patches, and skipping anti-malware checks when downloading and installing new files

- Removing cybersecurity design features to overcome technical challenges, such as adding an any → any rule to a firewall to solve connectivity issues

The deferral of activities, such as testing, to later in the project may save time up front. However, putting off testing can lead to problems that may cause delays. Resulting incidents may require last-minute, high-risk workarounds or changes that are not properly documented. Better planning and execution of testing earlier in the project should avoid the need for major changes during commissioning.

Red-Team Assessment

A red-team assessment is an important tool in the verification of cybersecurity posture. The assessment gets its name from military wargaming, where conflicts are simulated between an aggressor, the red team, and a defending force, the blue team. Red-team assessments in cybersecurity involve experts attempting to achieve a target, such as access to a certain machine or other resource. The exercise identifies vulnerabilities that can then be addressed. There are other methods of identifying vulnerabilities, such as penetration testing. Red-team assessments, if conducted properly, reflect realistic scenarios that may occur. These assessments identify vulnerabilities in technology, people, or processes.

Although the commissioning phase is hectic, it is an opportune time to conduct a red-team assessment. It is likely impractical to conduct such an assessment earlier in the project. Prior to commissioning, many of the systems and networks are not fully operational. For similar reasons, the scope of testing security controls during factory acceptance testing (FAT) may be limited and still not fully representative of the final facility. For instance, the physical security element of a red-team assessment is not indicative of the actual controls that will be in place. However, a red-team assessment also provides realistic training for the operations personnel acting as the blue team in the exercise.

Typical objectives for an automation system red-team assessment might be as follows:

- Gain remote access to the safety engineering workstation. This would test whether this critical device is properly segregated on the network. It will also indicate if the device is adequately protected by access controls. These controls include username and password as well as a second factor that requires physical presence, such as a fingerprint or key card.

- Gain local access to a control system HMI that allows set-point changes. This would test physical security, including locked rooms and cabinets. It also tests physical access to local factors, such as key cards. Figure 6-4 shows a Red-team member testing physical security controls as part of an assessment during a construction project.

Start-Up

The highest profile milestone in any project is start-up. Start-up is the culmination of the project and highly symbolic. In some cases, completion of the project may be strategically significant to the organization. Any delay may have a negative impact on share price. As a result, there is a great deal of focus on the start-up date. Start-up is the last chance to eliminate any cumulative delays created during the project. There will be significant pressure from management to make up this lost time and not miss the start-up date. As we saw with commissioning, time pressure can cause important steps to be skipped during the start-up phase.

Incident response continues to be critical during the start-up phase. High-profile projects may attract unwanted attention. For instance, environmental activists may seek to

Figure 6-4. Red team testing physical security controls during an assessment.

disrupt the operation of new oil and gas platforms using cyber methods. Nation-states may seek to attack major new pipeline projects to disrupt trade.

Even without such attention, a new facility is vulnerable during the early stages of operation. With a new facility and new systems, operators and technicians will not be familiar with *normal* behavior and will be slower to identify abnormal situations. Training and incident response exercises throughout a project prepare personnel for start-up and beyond. The project's incident response plan will be updated to reflect changes in circumstance and include new threats.

Handover and Closeout

Project teams plan their activities with the best of intentions. They map out milestones and payment schedules that address deliverables throughout the life of the project. Even so, the as-built documentation, by definition, can only be provided at the end of a project.

EPCs, vendors, and system integrators must manage their cashflow. For large capital projects, the contractors receive their biggest payments early in the process. The further along the project, the smaller the payments become. Payment for final deliverables may represent only 10% of the overall contract.

This emphasis on the early stages of a project creates a significant risk of poor quality or incomplete as-built documentation:

- Late and over-budget project teams must cut costs and reduce hours. An obvious place to start is final deliverables, especially if the savings outweigh the investment required.

- As the project nears completion, team members begin to disperse, moving on to new projects or roles. They take with them the knowledge needed to verify documentation.

Data quality is critical to every aspect of operations, including cybersecurity. Accurate drawings, hardware and software inventory lists, and other information such as Internet Protocol (IP) address allocations are instrumental in creating effective cybersecurity.

Cybersecurity tool vendors offer a variety of asset management solutions, but these are only as good as the data they incorporate. Scanning automation system networks using these tools shows a user what is found, but not whether it is supposed to be there. This approach may also miss devices connected via serial links or those behind industrial firewalls or other isolation components.

To provide good, quality data at handoff requires constant attention to oversight throughout the project. Drawings should have been produced during the design phase and constantly updated during the engineering, construction, and commissioning phases. Management of change processes should ensure that any change to the design is updated in documentation. Inventory lists, IP address allocations, and other similar documents should be produced early and maintained in the same manner. If this rigorous process is followed, only material such as final checklists, and confirmation that temporary connections or modifications are removed, should need to be gathered at the end of the project.

There is an international standard associated with asset planning that could help address the data challenge.

ISO 15926 is the standard for data integration, sharing, exchange, and handover.[108] There is an initiative based on this standard, led by the International Association of Oil & Gas Producers (IOGP), called Capital Facilities Information Handover Specification (CFIHOS).[109] CFIHOS utilizes the ISO 15926 definitions for a common language, format,

---

108 POSC Caesar Association, "An Introduction to ISO 15926," November 2011, accessed June 21, 2021, https://www.posccaesar.org/wiki/ISO15926Primer.

109 Capital Facilities Information Handover Specification, International Association of Oil & Gas Producers (IOGP), "More About CFIHOS," accessed June 21, 2021, https://www.jip36-cfihos.org/more-about-cfihos/.

and exchange of data. Utilizing the standard and the CFIHOS initiative has the potential to standardize the sharing of information across industries and projects. Ultimately, this would mean projects need only specify conformance to this standard. That would be a vast improvement over the current practice of projects defining their own standards and methods, many of which EPCs and other stakeholders may not completely follow.

Embed Cybersecurity Requirements in All Contracts

Contracts are an essential tool for managing performance of contractors and vendors on projects. To guarantee a secure end result, cybersecurity must be addressed in contractual requirements. This may sound obvious but, at the time of this writing, it is not that common. In some sectors where regulations exist (e.g., nuclear, chemical, electricity), those regulations form the basis of contractual requirements that must be met. As a result, awareness of these regulations and requirements is usually high.

In some sectors where cybersecurity posture is higher (e.g., oil and gas), asset owners provide a set of cybersecurity requirements to contractors and then conduct assessments on deliverables to confirm that these requirements are being met.

In sectors where cybersecurity posture is lower (e.g., water and wastewater), there may be no requirements issued or requirements may focus on IT security.

The use of contractual requirements for cybersecurity varies from country to country, depending on the regulatory environment.

Contracts should include cybersecurity requirements not only for systems, but also for project execution. As noted throughout this chapter, a typical project involves a wide range of cybersecurity risks. These risks can only be managed if the contractors and vendors are aware and prepared.

One important consideration for EPC projects is that the EPC will issue its own contracts to subcontractors and vendors. Asset owners should therefore ensure that a contract with the EPC stipulates what cybersecurity conditions must be passed on to subcontractors and others working for the EPC.

Key considerations for cybersecurity in contracts are as follows:

- Explicit milestones, deliverables, and payments related to cybersecurity. Examples include successful completion of design review(s), successful red-team assessment, and closure of cybersecurity punch-list items or actions. Payment terms for these milestones and deliverables must be significant enough that the EPC or vendor is motivated to complete them.

- Quality assurance of handover documentation. As noted earlier, data handed over in projects is often of poor quality. At the end of a project, the EPC or vendor may not be willing to invest the additional time required to clean up the data.

- Project-related cybersecurity activities. This would include a cybersecurity incident response plan that addresses how the EPC or vendor will deal with a cybersecurity incident on the project. The contract should explicitly state that the EPC or vendor is responsible for maintaining the cybersecurity posture of all equipment during the project life cycle. This includes the patch status of the operating system for servers and workstations, and the awareness of the EPC or vendor's employees and contractors.

Some asset owners now specify certified secure products in their contracts. The popularity of this approach will continue to grow, as a standard provides an independent means of assessing the security of products.

The ISA/IEC 62443 standards define compliance requirements for devices, systems, and even the development life cycle of automation system vendors. This is discussed in Chapter 5. This standards-based approach will significantly improve the cybersecurity posture of systems and projects. Look at how broad adoption of contracts requiring ISO 9000 compliance has improved quality and safety for hazardous equipment. This standards-based requirement is especially important in sectors or countries that lack well-defined standards or regulations.

Raise Awareness Within the Project Team

Cybersecurity awareness is essential throughout all phases of a project. It should be a requirement for all members of the team, regardless of whether they work for the asset owner, a vendor, or a system integrator. Vulnerabilities that project teams create on the job include the following:

- Poor design decisions due to lack of understanding of cybersecurity risk

- Failure to keep software up to date with the latest vendor patches

- Failure to maintain anti-malware protection

- Poor management of removable media

- Poor credential management

- Poor management of change

- Inadequate testing of security features

- Inadequate management of sensitive information

- Lack of a cybersecurity incident response procedure

Chapter 7, "What We Can Learn from the Safety Culture," covers awareness in detail.

Implement a Rigorous Oversight Process

As with any aspect of project execution, cybersecurity requires constant, rigorous oversight to ensure success. Key oversight elements are

- requirement verification,

- risk and issue management, and

- performance management.

Verification of Requirements

Contracts must include key requirements, but including them does not ensure the requirements will be met.

Governance, risk management, and compliance (GRC) defines how an organization approaches these practices. GRC can highlight areas of concern. However, the information produced from a GRC process is only as good as the data provided.

Like many aspects of cybersecurity, there is often too much emphasis on tools and not enough focus on the people and processes required for effective oversight. For example, in many large organizations assessment reports must be completed for each automation system. A GRC tool generates a questionnaire to check compliance against cybersecurity standards. It is based on questions such as:

- Is backup software in place?

- Is it possible to remotely access the safety system?

In most cases the response is either yes or no. Some questionnaires include multiple-choice questions; for example, for the question, "How often is user access reviewed?" the answers could be *review not performed, reviewed every 18 months, reviewed every 6 to 12 months,* or *reviewed every 3 to 6 months.*

The viability of the questionnaire depends on the quality of the assessor, the knowledge of the responder, and the availability of the information needed to answer the questions. These questionnaires are often performed late in the project life cycle. That means there is more information available, but it may be too late in the project to address nonconformances.

A better approach is to verify that the product vendor has completed the questionnaire *before* any contract is let. The vendor can also be asked to provide responses such as *compliant*, *optional at extra cost*, and *not compliant*.

It would still be necessary to validate that what is delivered meets the original requirements. That validation is easier to accomplish based on information provided by the vendor. The National Cyber Security Centre has produced compliance guidelines for Operators of Essential Services (OES), and Appendix B of these guidelines provides a helpful checklist that can be used if no specific questionnaire exists.[110]

Risk and Issue Management

The risks and issues being tracked by project leadership will likely reflect the major financial elements of the project. As already noted, these will be biased toward the construction or plant. Delays caused by unauthorized intrusion into vendor systems or theft of intellectual property are very real and have occurred elsewhere. These cybersecurity incidents have a significant impact on project finances and schedules. These risks should be tracked at the same level as, for example, delays to construction because of injury or death.

The risk of cybersecurity nonconformance should also be tracked at the same level as safety. Even in large organizations with well-defined automation system cybersecurity requirements, projects routinely hand over systems that do not meet all these requirements. The rationale is that the operations team will address the residual issues. Teams are under pressure to complete a project, and incomplete cybersecurity requirements do not usually prevent the system from operating. As a result, some organizations make a judgment call that the risk of nonconformance is less than the cost to delay the project start-up. As noted in Chapter 4, the quantification of cybersecurity risk is usually very poor. This lack of understanding can result in the wrong decision. More importantly, if cybersecurity is properly managed throughout the project life cycle, there should not be any nonconformance issues delaying start-up.

---

110 National Cyber Security Centre (NCSC), "NIS Compliance Guidelines for Operators of Essential Service (OES)," accessed June 21, 2021, https://www.ncsc.gov.ie/pdfs/NIS_Compliance_Security_Guidelines_for_OES.pdf.

Performance Management

Effectively tracking the performance of a contractor or vendor is critical to the success of a project. EPC projects typically use S-curves as a visual representation of planned and actual progress. Figure 6-5 shows a simple example of planned working hours per month (bars) and cumulative hours (line). The S-curve gets its name from the fact that the cumulative hours line is S-shaped. Depending on what is being tracked, the bars and lines might represent other metrics, such as deliverables (number of HMI screens completed, number of cabinets assembled, etc.).

The shape of the S-curve represents what should happen, in terms of progress, at any stage in the project: a slow start, ramping up to peak activity, followed by a decline as the remaining work tapers off toward completion.

The reality is often quite different. Figure 6-6 shows an example of plan versus forecast for a project activity. For various reasons, projects take longer to start than planned. The usual response is to show a forecast where more work is done later (or *backloaded*) to achieve the planned target date.

In terms of cybersecurity, such backloading is not advised. Still, it often happens, because cybersecurity is seen as a low risk to successful completion of the project. As already noted throughout this chapter, late identification of cybersecurity nonconformance can introduce delays to projects or can result in insecure systems being handed over to operations. This, in turn, exposes the organization to unnecessary risk.

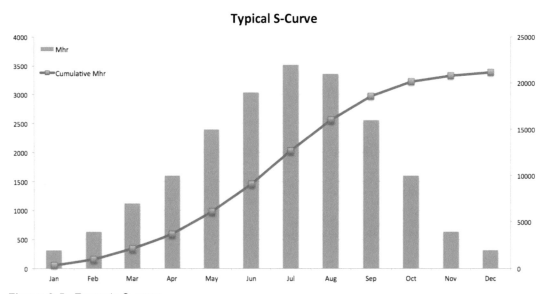

Figure 6-5. Example S-curve.

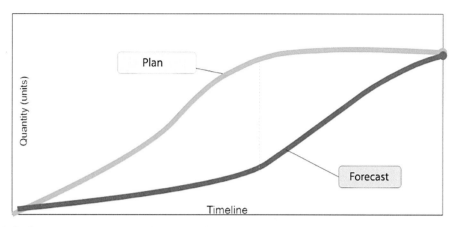

Figure 6-6. Planned and actual performance S-curves.

Examples of cybersecurity activities that are often delayed until later in project life cycles include the following:

- Update of operating system patches

- Physical implementation of a vendor remote access solution

- Configuration of application control or other antivirus protection

- Testing of multifactor authentication

All cybersecurity activities must be properly planned and resourced. They should not be backloaded.

Summary

Today projects that deliver new automation systems or enhancements to existing systems routinely introduce new cybersecurity vulnerabilities in organizations. In addition, the projects themselves contain vulnerabilities that can impact the organization. The lack of understanding of cybersecurity risks is a major factor, as is the failure to correctly manage cybersecurity. This chapter has identified the key factors for successfully managing cybersecurity:

- Secure senior project leadership support

- Embed cybersecurity throughout the project

- Embed cybersecurity requirements in all contracts

- Raise awareness within the project team

- Implement rigorous oversight processes

There are many things that organizations can leverage to improve results, including the following:

- Use certified secure products from certified vendors.

- Define security controls at the design stage to avoid costly, less effective, implementation later.

- Regularly review cybersecurity implementation progress in the project.

- Link milestones and payments to cybersecurity requirements.

- Ensure the project resourcing and time plan includes a regular cybersecurity update of equipment during execution (e.g., anti-malware, software upgrades/patches, backups).

- Include a plan for changing over all user accounts and test code, as well as removing vendor accounts, default accounts, and test software or configurations.

- Define a cybersecurity incident response plan for the project that includes all stakeholders, so a process is in place when an incident occurs during project execution.

- Provide regular cybersecurity awareness training for everyone on the project, including users, vendors, and integrators.

- Plan for an independent red-team assessment of the final as-built environment, incorporating realistic scenarios to provide additional assurance that security is in place as expected.

Cybersecurity is a critical element of operations and must be treated as such during a project.

7

What We Can Learn from the Safety Culture

Introduction

Cybersecurity awareness training is a common tool employed by many organizations. What constitutes awareness training and who receives it can vary considerably. Any cybersecurity awareness training is better than none, but training designed for those in information technology (IT) environments is not sufficient for those in operational technology (OT) environments. This distinction is lost in many organizations where training, like other aspects of cybersecurity, is managed by the IT function. Such generic training neglects the operational and cultural differences in OT facilities.

This chapter will identify the operational and cultural differences between an IT and an OT environment. Taking these differences into account, it will explore the essential elements of cybersecurity awareness training and monitoring required for an OT environment.

The Importance of Awareness

Visit any OT facility today and you will likely find several obvious cybersecurity policy violations or bad practices. Typical examples include the following:

- Poor physical security, such as unlocked equipment rooms or keys permanently left in equipment cabinet doors.

- Uncontrolled removable media used to transfer data.

- Poor electronic security, such as leaving user credentials visible. See Figure 7-1 for a real example of this bad practice.

Even in regulated industries, compliance with cybersecurity regulations is, at the time of this writing, not where it should be. In 2019, Duke Energy was fined $10 million by the North American Electric Reliability Corporation (NERC) for 127 violations of the NERC Critical Infrastructure Protection (CIP) regulations between 2015 and 2018.[111] Although this was an unusually large fine (consistent with a major regulatory violation), NERC continues to fine companies that fail to follow its cybersecurity regulations.

This is consistent with other reports. Interviewed by the *Wall Street Journal* for a report on the Duke Energy fine, security consultant Tom Alrich said, "The state of compliance is pretty rotten." Because he knew that Duke spent a lot of money on its critical infrastructure protections, Alrich added, "I really doubt they are much more insecure than anyone else."[112]

Figure 7-1. Control room console with user credentials visible on a permanent label.

---

111 See https://www.nerc.com/pa/comp/CE/Pages/Actions_2019/Enforcement-Actions-2019.aspx for details.

112 Rebecca Smith, "Duke Energy Broke Rules Designed to Keep Electric Grid Safe," *Wall Street Journal*, updated February 1, 2019, accessed June 21, 2021, https://www.wsj.com/articles/duke-energy-broke-rules-designed-to-keep-electric-grid-safe-11549056238.

The 127 violations relate to controls such as physical security, change control, access management, configuration management, documentation, information protection, and incident response, all of which are highly dependent on individual training, awareness, and behavior. Some of the violations actually related to gaps or failures in Duke Energy's cybersecurity awareness training program.

In July 2020, Duke Energy announced a $56 billion capital investment plan. This plan featured several forward-looking statements,[113] including this one referencing cybersecurity threats: "These factors include, but are not limited to: ...[t]he impact on facilities and business from a terrorist attack, cybersecurity threats, data security breaches, operational accidents, information technology failures or other catastrophic events, such as fires, explosions, pandemic health events or other similar occurrences."[114]

Even though Duke Energy's plan includes cybersecurity alongside well-known types of threats, it may not help the company's NERC CIP compliance. This compliance depends on the performance of its employees, their awareness of cybersecurity threats, and execution of the necessary mitigations.

Underestimating Risk

Skepticism is a significant factor in poor cybersecurity preparedness. By now, most individuals are familiar with one or more high-profile cybersecurity incidents; some even may have been impacted by one. Despite this growing awareness, it seems many people in OT environments feel cybersecurity is not their problem. Their views fall into one of two camps:

1. The likelihood of a cyber incident is low because either the organization is not a target, or it has not happened in the past.

2. The consequence of a cyber incident is low because many layers of protection are in place.

As noted in Chapter 4, "Measure to Manage Cybersecurity Risk," it is essential that organizations take a different approach to estimating the likelihood and consequences of cybersecurity risk in OT environments.

---

113 A "forward-looking statement" is a recognized term in US business law that is used to indicate, for example, plans for future operations or expectations of future events.
114 Duke Energy News Center, "Duke Energy Reaffirms Capital Investments in Renewables and Grid Projects to Deliver Cleaner Energy, Economic Growth," July 5, 2020, accessed June 21, 2021, https://news.duke-energy.com/releases/releases-20200705-6806042.

Empirical probability calculates a likelihood based on historical data. It is not well suited to providing future estimates when the historical data is sparse. Bayes's theorem is routinely used to estimate risk in finance (the risk of lending money to new borrowers) and medicine (the accuracy of a medical test). It can be used to estimate the likelihood of an event in situations with sparse historical data.

Using Monte Carlo simulation, it is possible to calculate the probability of an event and apply a confidence level. This simulation technique makes an allowance for uncertainty while providing an easily understood, quantitative estimate. In particular, applying the P10, P50, or P90 qualifiers will be familiar to anyone who uses these terms in schedule, cost, and other estimates, such as oil and gas reserves.

The security process hazard analysis (PHA) approach focuses organizations on process hazards, rather than control system and network equipment failures. Raising cybersecurity risks to the same level as safety risks will produce a more realistic view of the actual risk an organization faces. This approach also makes the risk "real" to those who understand the consequences best. Consider, for example, a cybersecurity incident on a turbine control system. This risk estimate should consider the consequences in terms of the turbine or the associated process—pump damage, bearing damage, loss of containment—rather than the failure of turbine control system equipment itself, such as the programmable logic controller (PLC) and human-machine interface (HMI).

A properly designed facility has multiple diverse layers of protection in place. However, well-publicized incidents such as Stuxnet and TRISIS should make it clear that the basic automation and safety system layers are at risk. The compromise of these *prevention* layers leaves only the *mitigation* layers, such as overpressure valves and disaster protection capabilities, to attenuate the consequences of an incident.

Consider the three examples described in Chapter 4:

1. It is highly likely that the Stuxnet malware found its way into a nuclear enrichment facility in Iran via infected removable media. The fact that the control system was not accessible to the outside world did not protect them.

2. Attackers used basic phishing techniques to gain access to internal networks and ultimately take control of operator workstations in three Ukrainian power distribution companies, none of which had incident response plans in place for a scenario that they did not believe possible.

3. Attackers would not have been able to modify the code on the safety controller in a Middle East petrochemical facility had the facility personnel kept the physical key switch on that device in run mode.

Consequence						Likelihood			
						Improbable (> 10 years)	Remote (Once in 10 years)	Occasional (Once a year)	Frequent (Once a month)
		Health/Safety	Environmental	Financial	Reputation and Public Disruption	Regulatory	1	2	3	4
Low	1	Injury or illness without a loss of a work day; Event requiring First Aid	Unfavorable impact but without any environmental harm or nuisance	Less than $10k	Public not aware	Limited impact with less than $10k in fines or penalties	1	2	3	4
Moderate	2	Injury or illness resulting in treatment by a doctor or hospitalization; Long term sickness over 3 days	Unreasonable impact resulting in environmental nuisance/cleanup	Between $10k and $100k	Local media coverage; Telephone complaints	Fines or penalties between $10k and $200k	2	4	6	8
High	3	Permanent injury or long term sickness over 3 months; Multiple serious injuries	Significant impact with localized environmental harm but not in an environmentally sensitive area	Between $100k and $1m	Extended local adverse media campaign; State media coverage	Fines or penalties totaling between $200k and $500k	3	6	9	12
Severe	4	Single or multiple deaths; Multiple permanent injuries	Major environmental harm caused in environmentally sensitive areas; Environmental damage causing a violation of law or regulation	Over $1m	National adverse media coverage	Officer jailed Fine or penalty over $500k	4	8	12	16

Figure 7-2. Applying realistic estimates of likelihood and consequence changes risk level.

Figure 7-2 shows the typical organization risk matrix from Chapter 4. The typical underestimate of likelihood and consequence results in risks in the lower left of the matrix. In cybersecurity risk assessment, underestimating likelihood occurs because there is a lack of historic data and an assumption that *it has not happened in the past so it will not happen in future*. Underestimating consequence occurs because of the failure to adequately take into account the process-based risk. Realistic estimates of likelihood, using statistical methods, and consequence, using process-based risk assessment, will almost certainly result in risks moving into the lower right of the matrix. The difference is dramatic, moving from *low* to *extreme* according to the definitions in this particular risk matrix.[115]

Human Error

In an article titled "The Sorry State of Cybersecurity Imagery," Eli Sugarman and Heath Wickline note that images online are "all white men in hoodies hovering menacingly over keyboards, green Matrix-style 1s and 0s, glowing locks and server racks, or some random combination of those elements—sometimes the hoodie-clad men even wear burglar masks. Each of these images fails to convey anything about either the importance or complexity of the topic."[116] It is therefore no surprise that most people's perception of a cybersecurity incident is limited.

---

115 This is for illustrative purposes only. Specific likelihood, consequence, and risk values will vary, but the deviation is likely to be as dramatic when more rigorous methods are used.
116 Eli Sugarman and Heath Wickline, "The Sorry State of Cybersecurity Imagery," July 25, 2019, accessed May 12, 2022, https://hewlett.org/the-sorry-state-of-cybersecurity-imagery/.

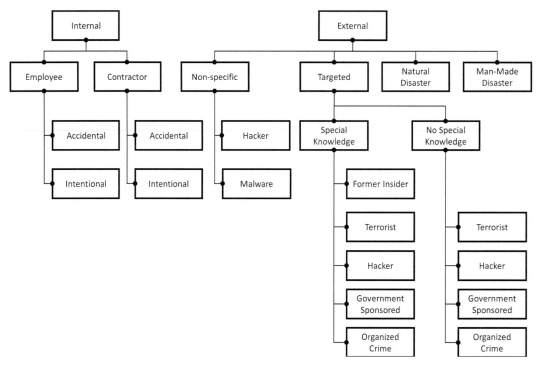

Figure 7-3. Taxonomy of threat sources.

Figure 7-3 shows a categorization of potential threat sources. Alongside the obvious sources—terrorist, hacker, organized crime, and disgruntled former employees—are accidental acts by well-meaning employees and contractors, as well as disasters, natural and man-made.

It is important to consider the entirety of threat sources when managing cybersecurity. Accidental and deliberate acts can have identical consequences. Such accidental acts include the following:

- Failure to comply with a procedure, such as those relating to anti-malware, account management, or removable media use

- Failure to maintain or test backups, resulting in an inability to restore a system after a disaster

- A device configuration mistake, such as the deployment of an incorrect firewall rule

Accidental acts are a significant contributor to the totality of cybersecurity incidents today and have been since record keeping began. In 2013, the Repository of Industrial

Security Incidents (RISI) identified 82% of industrial control system cybersecurity incidents as being unintentional.[117]

Looking more broadly at cybersecurity incidents, IBM's 2018 X-force Threat Intelligence Index provided a helpful visualization. Their research shows that the majority of cybersecurity incidents were caused by misconfiguration. IBM's 2020 X-force Threat Intelligence Index noted that:

> …the number of breached records jumped significantly in 2019 with over 8.5 billion records exposed—more than three times greater than 2018 year-over-year. The number one reason for this significant rise is that records exposed due to misconfigurations increased nearly tenfold year-over-year.[118] These records made up 86% of the records compromised in 2019. This is a stark departure from what we reported in 2018 when we observed a 52% decrease from 2017 in records exposed due to misconfigurations and these records made up less than half of total records.[119]

Even though the report noted a "decrease in the number of misconfiguration incidents in 2019 of 14%year-over-year," it also noted that "nearly three-quarters of the breaches where there were more than 100 million records breached were misconfiguration incidents."[120]

Figure 7-4 shows a bowtie diagram representing the potential threats to an organization with a comingled IT and OT network. These threats could result in a loss of visibility or control on OT systems, as well as exfiltration of sensitive information from IT systems or ransomware compromise of these systems.

Comingling of IT and OT resources, such as IT servers and workstations, closed-circuit television cameras, PLCs, and HMIs, is common, especially in organizations seeking to avoid the additional cost of deploying and managing separate IT and OT networks.

The *unauthorized access to IT network* and *unauthorized access to OT network* threats are mitigated by several controls, but in each case, there is the potential for accidental acts. These include *configuration error, weak password management, weak antivirus (AV)/patching regime*, and *intrusion detection system (IDS) alert failure* (i.e., a failure to act on an IDS alert).

---

117 Repository of Industrial Security Incidents, "2013 Report on Cyber Security Incidents and Trends Affecting Industrial Control Systems, Revision 1.0," June 15, 2013, available by request from RISI, https://www.risidata.com/
118 It is unclear whether this increase is due to better measurement or more human error, or both.
119 IBM Security, *IBM X-Force Threat Intelligence Index 2020*, 8, accessed June 21, 2021, https://www.scribd.com/document/451825308/ibm-x-force-threat-intelligence-index-2020-pdf.
120 IBM Security, *IBM X-Force Threat Intelligence Index 2020*.

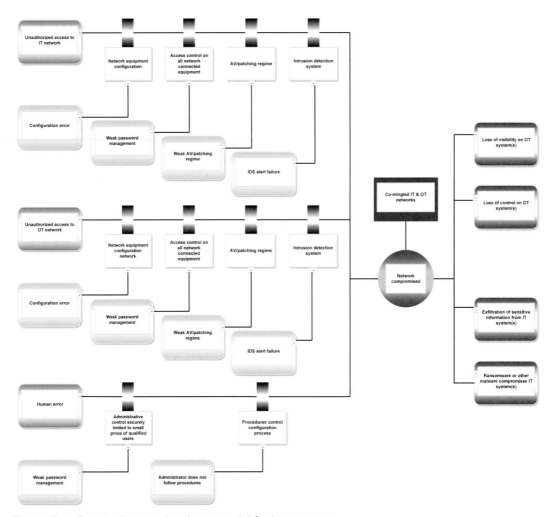

Figure 7-4. Bowtie diagram showing potential for human error.

The bowtie diagram also shows that the mitigations for the *human error* threat are heavily dependent on administrative controls. These include a well-managed access control process that limits elevated access to a small group of competent users, and rigorous procedures for tasks performed by users with elevated access.

As noted in Chapter 4, mitigating control effectiveness varies depending on the type of control. Administrative controls are among the weakest. This is reflected in the hierarchy of controls, repeated in Figure 7-5.

The potential for human error, and the limitations in mitigating this risk, highlight the importance of people in cybersecurity. No amount of technology or procedures can completely mitigate the potential for a human-initiated cybersecurity incident. This is borne out by an analysis of the initiating cause of high-profile cybersecurity incidents. Almost

Figure 7-5. The hierarchy of controls and its relationship to cybersecurity.

without exception, a human was involved, clicking on a link in a phishing email, failing to deploy patches, failing to follow removable media procedures, and so on.

Unfortunately, many organizations still try to address the cybersecurity challenge by deploying more and more technology and creating more and more rules. They do not recognize or address the significance of humans. Strict rules may provide the appearance that cybersecurity is under control. A bowtie diagram with many additional barriers will help support this argument. However, this approach can actually lead to complacency on the part of the individuals. Workers assume that adequate controls are in place, or that cybersecurity is someone else's job. Even individuals aware of the importance of cybersecurity may consider the threat mitigated by physical security, technical controls, and procedures. This attitude may result in a more casual approach to other controls, such as limiting electronic access and the use of removable media. A common example of this in OT environments is the deployment of universal serial bus (USB) locks on equipment such as HMIs or servers. Personnel will claim these controls are not necessary because the equipment is in locked cabinets inside secure rooms. In fact, it is not unusual to discover these rooms are not adequately secured, and the cabinets are left with keys in the locks. Even the keys themselves are commonly available, and the same key can usually open most cabinets from the same manufacturer.

Jessica Barker is the CEO of Cygenta, a cybersecurity provider specializing in assessment and awareness services. In her book *Confident Cyber Security*, she warns against the phrase "users are the weakest link." Instead, she argues that we should do more to understand the challenges users face and identify what causes them to take these risks.[121]

---

121 Jessica Barker, *Confident Cyber Security* (London: Kogan Page Limited, 2020), 91.

To highlight this issue, Barker presents a case study: A finance administrator receives an email from the company's chief executive officer (CEO) instructing him to transfer funds to an account. This transfer is urgently needed to secure the acquisition of a new business. The finance administrator feels pressured to respond promptly and transfers the funds without any further validation.[122] This may seem unlikely, yet this *CFO fraud*, or *whaling*,[123] is very real. Since 2013, more than $12 billion has been lost to whaling in the United States, United Kingdom, and Europe.[124] In one high-profile incident, a finance executive at the toy company Mattel transferred $3 million to cybercriminals. Mattel had a procedure where wire transfers required two signatures. The signature of the newly appointed CEO had been forged, and the finance executive did not do any further validation.[125]

In her book, Barker points to economists Richard Thaler and Daniel Kahneman for an insight into what drives otherwise rational, intelligent people to make such glaring mistakes. Thaler and Kahneman have separately won the Nobel Prize in economics for their research into behavioral economics and decision-making. Each has identified two systems of thinking in human behavior: Thaler calls them the *Automatic System* and *Reflective System*;[126] Kahneman describes them as *Fast* and *Slow*.[127] The automatic/fast system is an important element to thinking. It allows for rapid, autonomous reactions such as stepping out of the path of an approaching car. The reflective/slow system is more deliberate and involves complex decision-making. The application of these two systems creates several heuristics and biases. One that is directly applicable to cybersecurity is the availability heuristic. In this case, decisions are influenced by experience. Our perception of the consequences of an action are influenced by whether we recall those consequences. There are many other relevant considerations that help explain why people make bad decisions. These should be factored into policies, processes, and procedures, as well as cybersecurity awareness training. It is not enough to expect people to make good decisions. Organizations must be prepared for poor decisions as well.

---

122 Barker, *Confident Cyber Security*, 92–93.

123 Whaling is a method of targeting high-profile employees of organizations, not just chief financial officers, and derives its name from the *big catch* during phishing.

124 Dante Alighieri Disparte, "Whaling Wars: A $12 Billion Financial Dragnet Targeting CFOs," *Forbes*, December 6, 2018, accessed May 12, 2022, https://www.forbes.com/sites/dantedisparte/2018/12/06/whaling-wars-a-12-billion-financial-dragnet-targeting-cfos/?sh=7d0da85a7e52.

125 Darren Pauli, "Barbie-Brained Mattel Exec Phell for Phishing, Sent $3m to China," *The Register*, April 6, 2016, accessed May 12, 2022, https://www.theregister.com/2016/04/06/chinese_bank_holiday_foils_nearperfect_3_million_mattel_fleecing.

126 Richard H. Thaler and Cass R. Sunstein, *Nudge: Improving Decisions About Health, Wealth, and Happiness* (New Haven, CT: Yale University Press, 2008).

127 Daniel Kahneman, *Thinking, Fast and Slow* (New York: Farrar, Straus and Giroux, 2011).

Supporting the Right Behaviors

A literature review conducted by the Royal Holloway University of London for the UK Cabinet Office noted that awareness is not always sufficient to drive the correct behavior. One example is a password policy. Research identified in the review noted that password policies can be too demanding to manage or may interfere with productivity. For example, to keep track of multiple accounts, users may write down and reuse passwords.[128]

Jessica Barker notes that "the burden for security often falls to the end user." She goes on to say that it is "not fair to ask people to add security" in the same way that we "do not ask people to make sure the soft furnishings they buy are fire resistant or the car they rent has been safety-tested."[129]

Organizations identify security controls, define policies and procedures, and provide awareness training. They must also provide realistic, workable solutions that allow personnel to comply while maintaining the necessary level of productivity. It is unfair, and unrealistic, to expect personnel to bear the burden for security. They must do their part, but with organizational support. This support should include the following:

- The tools necessary to maintain security, such as password management tools, secure file transfer facilities, and secure, but practical, authentication methods.

- The training required to understand cybersecurity management, and the important role training plays in its success.

- The time needed to maintain security. The whaling examples show that actions such as the transfer of funds require time for thorough validation. It is unreasonable to expect anyone to approve such transfers without adequate notice. Similarly, many automation system technicians are routinely expected to take on additional cybersecurity-related responsibilities, such as patch management, anti-malware control, and access control, with little acknowledgment of the time, effort, and training required to perform these duties. This is considered further in Chapter 8, "Safeguarding Operational Support."

The Safety Culture

As noted in Chapter 2, "What Makes Industrial Cybersecurity Different?," IT and OT cultures are distinct. Whereas modern IT is intentionally experimental (the *fail-fast*

---

128 A. Ertan and G. Crossland, *Everyday Cyber Security in Organizations* (Royal Holloway University of London, 2018), 23.
129 Barker, *Confident Cyber Security*, 69.

concept), OT culture is focused on safety, resisting change where possible to avoid introducing unnecessary risk. For those working in OT environments, this safety culture is helpful in cybersecurity awareness training.

James Reason, professor emeritus of psychology at the University of Manchester, is the creator of the *Swiss cheese model* of accident causation. He believes an effective safety culture requires a constant high level of respect for anything that might defeat safety systems. He says the key is "not forgetting to be afraid." Well-designed systems with multiple layers of protection are designed to ensure that no single failure will lead to an accident. Such systems result in an "absence of sufficient accidents to steer by." This eats away at the desired state of "intelligent and respectful wariness."[130]

Reason says organizations should not think they are safe because there is no information to say otherwise. This mind-set leads to less concern about poor work practices or conditions. It may even reduce unease about identified deficiencies in layers of protection. The same thinking should be applied to cybersecurity. As noted earlier in this chapter, underestimation of cybersecurity risk and overconfidence in the layers of protection lead to a lack of concern. Left unchecked, this lack of concern can be expressed in the acceptance of bad practices such as use of unapproved removable media, leaving cabinets unlocked, leaving controllers open to remote programming, and poor account management.

E. Scott Geller, an alumni distinguished professor at Virginia Tech's Center for Applied Behavior Systems, has written of a "total safety culture" (TSC) achieved through implementing applied behavioral techniques.[131]

Geller says that building and maintaining an effective safety culture is an intentional process that requires the successful completion of several steps. These include familiar themes that most organizations employ, such as articulating values (e.g., "safety is our number one concern") and establishing expected behaviors (setting policies and procedures regarding how activities are to be conducted). Geller's TSC approach also emphasizes the importance of themes that are less common, or are underappreciated:

- Investing resources, including sufficient time, equipment, staff, and intra-organizational support

---

130 James Reason, "Achieving a Safe Culture: Theory and Practice," *Work & Stress: An International Journal of Work, Health and Organisations* 12, no. 3 (1998): 302, accessed June 21, 2021, https://www.tandfonline.com/doi/abs/10.1080/02678379808256868.

131 E. S. Geller, "10 Leadership Qualities for a Total Safety Culture," *Professional Safety*, May 2020, accessed June 21, 2021, http://campus.murraystate.edu/academic/faculty/dfender/OSH650/readings/Geller—10%20Leadership%20Qualities%20for%20a%20Total%20Safety%20Culture.pdf.

- De-incentivizing undesired behaviors, such as enforcing consequences for inappropriate safety actions

- Incentivizing desired behaviors, such as recognition, awards, and promoting social norms

- Continuous improvement, including reviewing all incidents and updating policies, procedures, and training as necessary

Geller defines the 10 leadership qualities required to support TSC. These include qualities overlooked by organizations in their management of cybersecurity:

- **Focus on process, not outcome** – There is a tendency in most organizations to identify metrics and then look only at the numbers, not the behaviors behind those numbers. This also creates a culture where it is preferable to avoid bad news, such as near misses. Geller says that leaders must "hold people accountable for accomplishing proactive process activities that can prevent injuries," and this applies equally to cybersecurity incidents. Encouraging the reporting of cybersecurity near misses, such as leaving controllers in an insecure state, will help to improve the process and create a more secure culture.

- **Promote ownership** – According to Geller, leaders must allow for self-directed behavior, rather than simple compliance with edicts. In the latter case, employees may comply if they are being monitored, but in the absence of management, their behavior changes. For example, people will wear personal protective equipment at work but not at home, even when performing similarly hazardous tasks. This is relevant to cybersecurity because poor behaviors outside work can have a direct impact on security. For example, a worker transfers files at home between a personal computer and a USB drive without adequate antivirus scanning. If the worker then uses the USB drive on the job, it could transfer malware to operational systems.

Two important tools in the safety culture are the "site safety briefing" and the "toolbox talk." Both involve raising awareness of safety, focusing on the hazards that are present on-site or in a particular task. The safety briefing tends to be a prepared video or presentation. It gives an overview of the site, the main hazards, and the emergency procedures that must be followed. The toolbox talk may be an informal discussion about a safety topic. It is typically conducted before starting a task or at the beginning of the workday. The toolbox talk will focus on the hazards associated with a particular task and the controls that must be in place to perform the task.

Site safety briefings should include a discussion of cybersecurity hazards and required behaviors, for example, advising site visitors that uncontrolled removable media may not be used. The site safety briefing should also include a discussion of the site's cybersecurity incident response procedure.

Toolbox talks should also cover cybersecurity issues, for example, the risk of performing a software update on a machine and "controls" such as performing a backup before making any changes.

The more cybersecurity is embedded into the safety culture, the more likely it is to be adopted as an integral part of operations rather than an afterthought.

The First Line of Defense

The phrase "users are the weakest link" underestimates the challenges users face in dealing with cybersecurity. Organizations recognize that badly trained users operating with a lack of procedures, tools, or management support are likely to initiate most, if not all, cybersecurity incidents.

Conversely, well-trained users with good procedures, tools, and management support will act as an organization's first line of defense against a cybersecurity incident. Technology, such as firewalls, antivirus software, and network monitoring are essential controls. Users should be considered as equally valid controls. Combined, these constitute a defense-in-depth approach to cybersecurity management.

Don Merrell worked as an emergency medical technician at an agribusiness plant for J.R. Simplot Co. He responded to emergencies and injuries in the plant. In his work, Merrell noticed that almost every injury was due to unsafe conditions or risky behavior. This prompted him to write safety poems and limericks that have become staples in hazardous workplaces around the world. Probably his most famous poem is "I Chose to Look the Other Way," which ends with:

> *If you see a risk and walk away,*
> *Then hope you never have to say,*
> *"I could have saved a life that day,*
> *But I chose to look the other way."*

However, his poem "It's Up to Me" provides an even more appropriate message for users and their essential role in cybersecurity management, if the safety terms are replaced with their cybersecurity equivalents:

> *I want a workplace, that's Injury Free*
> *And if that's going to happen, then it's up to me.*

I can't take for granted, that anyone,
Has done all the things, that I should have done.

I must, take the time, with each task I do,
To look for the hazards, and think the job through.
To check the procedures and follow them all
And reject taking shortcuts, no matter how small.

When I walk through the workplace, I must stay alert
To watch for those things, that could get people hurt.
And if I see a hazard, I won't rest until,
I have made the thing safe, or know someone will.

I must question each unsafe behavior I see,
And encourage all others, to do that for me.
I must always give safety, the best I can do.
And expect that performance of all others too.

I must always remember to let people see,
That the things they do safely, is important to me.
Every act is important, no matter how small.
For the safety of one, is the safety of all.

We can all have a workplace that's injury free
If we each one Commit, to Making It Be,

If we all do our part, and each of us see,

If It's Going to Happen, - Then It's Up to Me.[132]

Users may be the weakest link, but they are the first line of defense for any organization. To be effective, they must be aware of the critical role they play.

Training and Competency

Training and Competence in the Orgainzation

Organizations approach cybersecurity training in a variety of ways. Some create their own material, and some use specialist training providers. There are advantages to

---

132 "It's Up to Me" and the extract from "I Chose to Look the Other Way" are reprinted with the permission of the author, Don Merrell. Contact Don Merrell at donmerrell@hotmail.com to inquire about the use of his poems or to comment on their impact.

each approach. Custom material can be made specific to an organization. It may be more relevant, but the material may lack the deep insights and broader experience of a specialist provider. A good compromise is to use a specialist training provider to customize material for the organization.

No matter how the training is created and provided, it must cover all the required skills and knowledge.

A great deal of excellent guidance is available for organizations to use in developing their training programs. The US Department of Labor's Automation Competency Model (ACM), created in 2008, has been updated regularly, using subject matter experts from the International Society of Automation (ISA) and elsewhere.[133] The ACM overview is shown in Figure 7-6. Each numbered block is a specific area of competency. Block 5.6 covers industrial automation and control systems cybersecurity. The specific skills and knowledge for this area of competency are described in the accompanying documentation.

The blocks in the ACM should not be considered in isolation. Being effective in automation systems cybersecurity requires the skills and knowledge defined in other blocks in the ACM. Furthermore, most organizations have a mixture of IT and OT personnel who have some role to play in automation systems cybersecurity. Each role will need a minimum standard of competency that covers a variety of areas.

To demonstrate this, consider Table 7-1. It provides a simplified competency matrix with a set of competency areas (found in the ACM). These have been categorized as *information technology, operational technology,* and *emerging technology.* Some generic job roles have been provided to demonstrate the mapping.

Each organization should produce its own competency matrix. The following are key considerations when doing so:

- Every role needs the same basic awareness training.

- Certain areas of competency must be explicitly identified and not merged. For instance, IT emergency response is different from OT emergency response.

---

133 Career Onestop Competency Model Clearing House, "Automation Competency Model," accessed June 21, 2021, https://www.careeronestop.org/competencymodel/competency-models/automation.aspx.

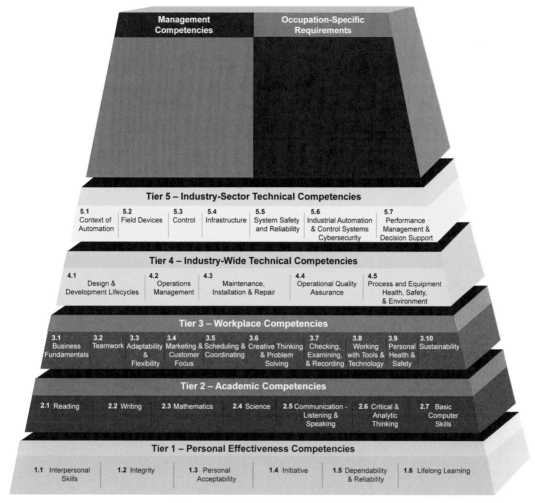

Figure 7-6. The US Department of Labor ACM.

- IT roles need more insight into OT aspects, such as concepts, architectures, standards, and emergency response.

- Managers and engineers must keep abreast of emerging technologies, such as Industry 4.0.

Training and Competence in the Supply Chain

Cybersecurity training and competency are not limited to the employees of an organization. The cybersecurity risk chain presented in Chapter 4 shows that an organization's risks are an accumulation of factors introduced throughout the supply chain. Focusing all efforts on the facility, procedures, and employees neglects the earlier parts of the supply chain. This is akin to focusing only on mitigating layers of protection without any attention to the preventive layers.

Table 7-1. Example competency matrix.

Role	Information Technology											Operational Technology								Emerging Technology		
	Basic Awareness	Security Risk Management	IT Architecture	Identify	Protect	Detect	Respond	Recover	Counter Threat and Intelligence	Certification	Ethical Hacking	OT Concepts	OT Architectures	Safety	Physical Security	Standards	Operations	Process Risk Management	Emergency Response	Industry 4.0 Architectures	Cognitive Computing/Big Data	Security Technologies
IT cybersecurity manager	X	X	X	X	X	X	X	X	X	X	X					X				X	X	X
IT cybersecurity engineer	X	X	X	X	X	X	X	X	X	X	X					X				X	X	X
IT cybersecurity technician	X	X	X	X	X	X	X	X								X						
OT cybersecurity manager	X	X	X	X	X	X	X	X	X	X	X	X	X	X	X	X	X	X	X	X	X	X
OT cybersecurity engineer	X	X	X	X	X	X	X	X	X	X	X	X	X	X	X	X	X	X	X	X	X	X
OT cybersecurity technician	X	X	X	X	X	X	X	X				X	X	X	X	X	X	X	X			
OT operations engineer	X			X	X	X	X	X				X	X	X	X	X	X	X	X			
OT operations technician	X			X	X	X	X	X				X	X	X	X	X	X	X	X			

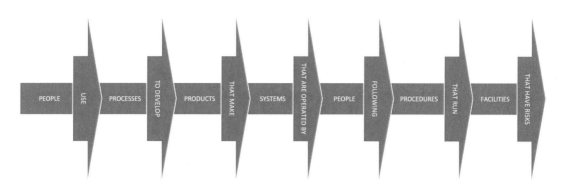

Figure 7-7. The cybersecurity risk chain.

Figure 7-7 shows the risk chain as it applies to the systems and devices used to monitor and control the facility.

Automation system product vendors (as well as system integrators and other service providers) must understand cybersecurity so that they can design products securely. Their organization must have secure development procedures in place to validate that products are secure. These development procedures will also improve the rigor in development and testing, providing a higher quality, more reliable solution.

One way to provide assurance of this competence is to purchase independently certified secure products and systems from certified vendors. Compliance with ANSI/ISA-62443-2-1 requires that vendors be adequately trained and follow rigorous processes.

In the absence of independent certification, organizations should embed contractual requirements covering cybersecurity awareness, development procedures, and incident response. This is discussed further in Chapter 6, "Pitfalls of Project Delivery," and Chapter 8.

Organizations should consider reviewing risk chains for other aspects of their supply chain. These aspects include service providers, raw material suppliers, and logistics providers. As supply chains become more integrated, a failure of cybersecurity management by a third party can result in serious consequences for an organization. The Target and Saudi Aramco examples mentioned in Chapter 2 illustrate this point.

Continuous Evaluation

Training and competency are not one-time exercises. Personnel need continuous learning to ensure they are aware of changes to policies and procedures, risks, and mitigating controls. In addition, there must be a system of monitoring to ensure that training is effective.

The concept of leading and lagging indicators was discussed in Chapter 3, "Creating Effective Policy." Monitoring near misses and performing regular audits verify that employees are following their training and procedures. This creates leading indicators that can be adjusted so that the resulting lagging indicators are within expectations. For example, if employees have training outstanding, they can be prompted to complete this. Observations and audits will show if training must be adjusted.

Reporting on leading and lagging indicators would be based on the security triangle shown in Figure 7-8. Leading indicators include:

- **Training completion rates** – This should include the periodic renewal of training material. Most learning management systems provide reporting on training completion.

- **Clear workspace checks** – Periodically checking employee work areas helps to gauge how well employees are following good cybersecurity practices. Common failings include leaving computers unlocked when not present, leaving sensitive documents on display, and leaving devices such as smartphones and USB drives unattended. Attention to these details helps to drive an improved security culture.

- **Phishing test results** – There are a variety of third-party services available to send employees simulated phishing emails, such as fake LinkedIn requests, invoice approval requests, or requests to enter credentials. Although employees

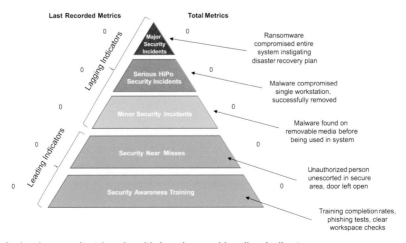

Figure 7-8. A simple security triangle with lagging and leading indicators.

can become familiar with this process, it still provides a useful measure of how well people are recognizing social engineering attacks.

Basic phishing test results reveal the percentage of people clicking on a phishing test email. To make these results more meaningful, they could be combined with the number of real phishing emails received. This information can be obtained by enabling employees to report suspicious emails. This combination helps create a more useful metric, called the phishing incident credible occurrence (PICO) score.[134]

Figure 7-9 provides an example for a fictitious organization. The bars show the number of phishing emails received/reported by users and the number of test emails clicked by users—both are shown as a percentage of the population of users. The line shows the PICO score, which is the product of the number of phishing emails received/reported by users and the number of test emails clicked by users as a percentage of the population.

The organization can now create a trend line for PICO, which, in this example, shows a steady increase toward three credible phishing incidents per month. This number should be more meaningful to individuals. It is similar in structure to well-known safety HiPo (high-potential) events they might be familiar with.

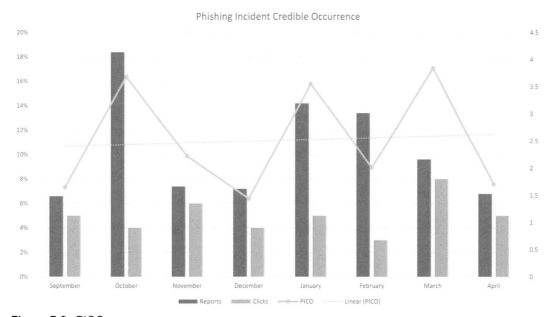

Figure 7-9. PICO.

134 My thanks to Collin Kleypas for the original idea.

Summary

Cybersecurity is constantly in the news, so it may seem reasonable to believe that people have a good awareness of the cybersecurity risks their organizations face. However, evidence indicates otherwise as incidents continue to occur. This trend is primarily driven by people failing to enforce good cybersecurity management practices. Even in regulated industries, organizations still fail to meet cybersecurity management requirements. This is largely due to personnel not following procedures, and a lack of oversight and enforcement by management.

A major factor underpinning this problem is that people underestimate their organization's cybersecurity risk. This might be because they have no quantitative means of measuring the likelihood or consequence of an incident. It can also be a result of complacency, believing that the other layers of protection will prevent any serious consequences.

Human behavior must be understood if organizations are to provide good awareness training for their employees. Humans tend to use their automatic (or fast) system of thinking when taking actions, whereas the reflective (or slow) system allows time for more deliberation. This comes into play in cases such as approving a large financial transfer resulting from a whaling attack.

Additional controls can be deployed to minimize the consequences of such mistakes, but it is clear from the hierarchy of controls that effectiveness varies. Some administrative controls can be circumvented if employees are pressured into acting quickly or have limited resources. To overcome this issue, organizations must offer the necessary time and resources for employees to perform their roles. Organizations must provide the right tools to allow them to do this securely and safely, while still being efficient. This situation is analogous to the organizational safety culture.

Having considered the negative aspects of people and their role in cybersecurity incidents, note that the same people are also the first line of defense. This is not limited to personnel within the organization. The entire supply chain is full of individuals who can be effective controls in the management of cybersecurity, as long as they are trained to be aware of the following:

- Why cybersecurity is so important

- How a cybersecurity incident can lead to a serious safety or operational issue

- What cybersecurity controls are in place, and what happens if they fail

- What part each person plays in maintaining a good cybersecurity posture for the organization

Cybersecurity training in the OT environment should not be limited to IT security concepts only. Aspects such as OT architectures, safety, physical security, standards, operations, risk management, and emergency response are essential for everyone. This includes workers from IT and OT backgrounds who are involved with cybersecurity management in the OT environment.

Along with awareness training, it is essential that organizations identify and monitor leading and lagging indicators. Again, the safety culture helps by identifying such metrics as near misses, HiPo incidents, and credible occurrence likelihood. These metrics can be readily converted to cybersecurity equivalents.

In summary, cybersecurity is heavily dependent on individuals. This sentiment is best summed up by a verse of the poem "It's Up to Me," modified by Don Merrell:[135]

We can all have a workplace that's cybersecurity incident free
If we each one Commit, to Making It Be,
If we all do our part, and each of us see,
If It's Going to Happen, - Then It's Up to Me.

---

135 I am indebted to Don Merrell for providing this modified verse from his poem "It's Up to Me." It is reprinted with the permission of the author, Don Merrell. Contact Don Merrell at donmerrell@ hotmail.com to inquire about the use of his poems or to comment on their impact.

8

Safeguarding Operational Support

Introduction

One of the distinguishing features of operational technology (OT) is the operational life of the equipment. Information technology (IT) is refreshed every 18 months to 3 years to keep pace with the demands of users and their applications. Conversely, OT equipment is designed for a specific, limited set of functions. Once deployed, there is little desire to change it. Recall the adage, "If it ain't broke, don't fix it," from Chapter 2, "What Makes Industrial Cybersecurity Different?" In fact, the high-availability environments where OT exists create a unique operational support culture, one that does not lend itself to good cybersecurity management. Shortcomings include the following:

- Taking devices out of service to upgrade with critical software or firmware fixes. This practice may involve significant downtime and increased risk during restart. Many automation systems today run with operating systems or applications that are no longer supported.

- Interfering with the operation of systems that may involve proprietary hardware, software, or communications protocols. This can create undesirable situations that are difficult to diagnose without specialist knowledge. This is exacerbated by aging systems. Each year it becomes more difficult to find specialists as experienced members of the workforce retire. This paucity of institutional knowledge makes it difficult, if not impossible, to introduce security mitigations such as network monitoring or application control. Lack of documentation is a significant factor in this issue.

- Long-standing operational practices must change to improve security. It can be difficult to make such changes if the system, and supporting practices, have been in service for several years—for example, the use of shared user accounts where the password has never been changed, or the use of insecure remote access methods in business-critical functions.

- There may be no practical means to restore an aged system in the event of a cybersecurity incident. In some facilities, the asset owner may not even have copies of the software required to restore the system. The vendor may no longer be in business.

OT is seen as a means to an end. It exists only to support operational processes and activities. Those operations typically involve hazards. Severe consequences such as death or injury to personnel or members of the public, harm to the environment, damage to equipment, loss of production, regulatory violations, and brand damage may result. Consequently, safety is a major concern in such operations. Cybersecurity, despite being a potential initiating cause in these hazards, is not respected in the same way as safety is. Many organizations begin meetings or presentations with the refrain that safety is the number one concern. But in those same meetings, there may be comments to the effect that "We have more important priorities than cybersecurity." This opinion is often shared by people in leadership positions. Clearly, there is still much to do before cybersecurity receives the attention it requires in operational environments.

Security technologist Bruce Schneier, author of the 2011 book *Secrets and Lies: Digital Security in a Networked World*, has a theory about why security is not a major factor for organizations. In his blog he writes about network security in particular:

> Historically most organizations haven't spent a lot of money on network security. Why? Because the costs have been significant: time, expense, reduced functionality, frustrated end users. (Increasing security regularly frustrates end users.) On the other hand, the costs of ignoring security and getting hacked have been, in the scheme of things, relatively small. We in the computer security field like to think they're enormous, but they haven't really affected a company's bottom line. From the CEO's perspective, the risks include the possibility of bad press and angry customers and network downtime—none of which is permanent. And there's some regulatory pressure, from audits or lawsuits, which adds additional costs. The result: a smart organization does what everyone else does, and no more.

He then notes, "Things are changing; slowly, but they're changing. The risks are increasing, and as a result spending is increasing."[136]

---

136 Bruce Schneier, "Secrets and Lies: Introduction to the Second Edition," Schneier on Security blog, accessed June 21, 2021, https://www.schneier.com/books/secrets-and-lies-intro2.

Things certainly are changing. In May 2020, Blackbaud, a cloud software provider, was the victim of a ransomware attack and data breach. Blackbaud managed data for a wide variety of organizations. The company's own publicity claims its customers include more than 25,000 organizations in more than 60 countries. It serves arts and cultural organizations, corporations, faith communities, foundations, healthcare organizations, higher education institutions, individual change agents, K–12 schools, and nonprofit organizations.[137] The data breach affected, among others, at least 6 million individuals whose healthcare information was exfiltrated.[138] Blackbaud ultimately paid the ransom in return for access to its customers' data and a promise that the exfiltrated information was destroyed. This was just the beginning of the consequences for Blackbaud. As of November 2020, it was the defendant in 23 consumer class-action lawsuits.[139]

In his blog, Schneier also discusses why vendors "spend so little effort securing their own products."

> We in computer security think the vendors are all a bunch of idiots, but they're behaving completely rationally from their own point of view. The costs of adding good security to software products are essentially the same ones incurred in increasing network security—large expenses, reduced functionality, delayed product releases, annoyed users—while the costs of ignoring security are minor: occasional bad press, and maybe some users switching to competitors' products. The financial losses to industry worldwide due to vulnerabilities in the Microsoft Windows operating system are not borne by Microsoft, so Microsoft doesn't have the financial incentive to fix them. If the CEO of a major software company told his board of directors that he would be cutting the company's earnings per share by a third because he was going to really—no more pretending—take security seriously, the board would fire him. If I were on the board, I would fire him. Any smart software vendor will talk big about security, but do as little as possible, because that's what makes the most economic sense.[140]

This too is changing.

In December 2020, news broke of a major compromise of US federal government and Fortune 500 companies who used software from SolarWinds, a network management software vendor. The incident arose from a SolarWinds software update that contained malicious code. Users who applied the update, from March 2020, were exposed to the vulnerability. This potentially allowed attackers access to their network. It is

137 Blackbaud, "Cloud Software Built for the World's Most Inspiring Teams," accessed June 21, 2021, https://www.blackbaud.com/.

138 Marianne Kolbasuk McGee, "Blackbaud Ransomware Breach Victims, Lawsuits Pile Up," BankInfo Security, Information Security Media Group, September 24, 2020, accessed June 21, 2021, https://www.bankinfosecurity.com/blackbaud-ransomware-breach-victims-lawsuits-pile-up-a-15053.

139 Maria Henriquez, "Blackbaud Sued After Ransomware Attack," *Security* magazine, November 6, 2020, accessed June 21, 2021, https://www.securitymagazine.com/articles/93857-blackbaud-sued-after-ransomware-attack.

140 "Schneier, "Secrets and Lies: Introduction to the Second Edition."

estimated that 18,000 users applied the update. As of January 2021, it was unclear just how extensive the incident was.[141] Recall also the Saipem incident discussed in Chapter 6, "Pitfalls of Project Delivery." As asset owners increase their security, attackers will target the weakest link in the supply chain. As with the Blackbaud example, the risk profile is changing quickly. This may force asset owners and vendors to recognize the importance of cybersecurity to their operations.

Making Cybersecurity a Key Factor

Chapter 3, "Creating Effective Policy," identified the foundations for making cybersecurity a key factor:

- Establish the governance infrastructure.

- Assign senior management representation.

- Allocate clear ownership and resources.

- Establish good oversight.

- Communicate to the organization.

Communicating to the organization is one of the most important ways to raise and maintain the importance of cybersecurity. As with safety, as soon as management stops treating it as the number one priority, employees will respond accordingly.

One important tool that can be leveraged for communication and management of cybersecurity in industrial environments is the barrier model.

Barrier Model Analysis and Visualization

Barrier model analysis is widely used in process industries to help analyze and visualize the status of the layers of protection required to maintain a safe operation.

Organizations may use different means to visualize their layers of protection. One approach is to use bowtie diagrams, such as those shown in Chapter 4, "Measure to Manage Cybersecurity Risk." Another is to use the Swiss cheese model. This approach was originally proposed by James Reason, professor emeritus of psychology at the University of Manchester. The methodology is simple: a bank of Swiss cheese slices represents a set of barriers to an incident or accident. The holes signify potential failures.

---

141 David E. Sanger, Nicole Perlroth, and Eric Schmitt, "Scope of Russian Hack Becomes Clear: Multiple U.S. Agencies Were Hit," *New York Times,* December 14, 2020, accessed June 21, 2021, https://www.nytimes.com/2020/12/14/us/politics/russia-hack-nsa-homeland-security-pentagon.html.

A failure of one of the barriers may not be sufficient to cause an accident: however, should a series of failures occur across several barriers, there is the potential for the holes to "line up" and an incident to occur. A simple example is shown in Figure 8-1.

It is possible to automatically read data from systems and aggregate it in accordance with the layers of protection arrangements. The Swiss cheese model can provide those responsible with a highly visual illustration. Figure 8-2 shows a typical example. Barrier color is calculated based on maintenance and risk data from control of work and work management systems and indicates the following:

- Green: Healthy.

- Yellow: Impaired barrier with two or more additional layers of protection, for example, suitable and sufficient mitigation measures applied.

- Red: Impaired barrier(s) related to a single hazardous event with one layer of protection or requirements of manual intervention.

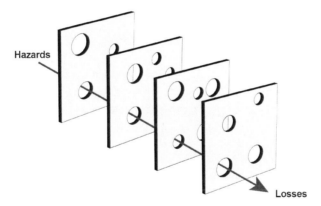

Figure 8-1. Simplistic example of the Swiss cheese model.

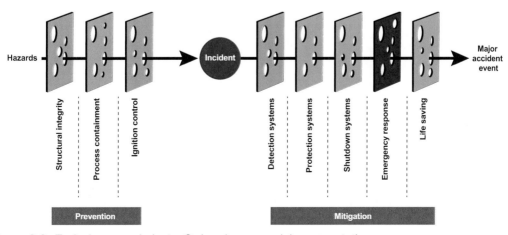

Figure 8-2. Typical process industry Swiss cheese model representation.

In this example, the organization used this tool for communication at four levels within the company:

- **Daily/weekly at the facility** – Informing the overall facility manager about the condition of the installation so it can assess suitability to continue operations.

- **Biweekly with the facility operations teams** – Informing the facility operations manager of the status of the installation and the progress of ongoing remedial scopes, and providing the opportunity to prioritize and escalate issues with teams.

- **Monthly within the business unit** – Providing a view of current asset integrity and status of all operated assets' safety-critical elements and barriers to major accident hazards. This provides the management team with a clear view of the progress being made toward remediation of barrier impairments.

- **Monthly at the overall organization leadership team level** – Providing the leadership team with a management overview of asset condition.

For each level, the key question is: *Are we still safe to operate?*

Integrating cybersecurity into such a reporting tool helps to make cybersecurity a key factor. First, consider Figure 8-3, a barrier representation of the typical cybersecurity controls discussed in Chapter 4 and Chapter 5, "Standardized Design and Vendor Certification."

On its own, this barrier representation can be helpful, especially if the status of the barriers can be determined by reading data from operational systems.

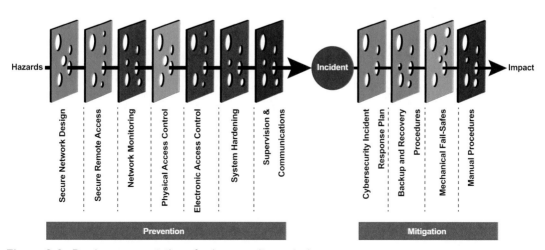

Figure 8-3. Barrier representation of cybersecurity controls.

The real power of this approach comes if the barrier representation shown in Figure 8-2 is updated to include a *cybersecurity* barrier. Now the barrier representation reviewed at all four levels in the aforementioned organization clearly shows the status of cybersecurity at the facility. The question *Are we still safe to operate?* must now include the status of cybersecurity.

People Management

As noted throughout this book, technology is not the only facet of the cybersecurity challenge. People and processes are equally as important as technology, and in some cases more important.

Many assume the threat of cybersecurity attack comes from individual hackers, organized crime, or nation-states. In fact, for most organizations, the greatest threat of cybersecurity incidents comes from inside the organization itself. This threat comes in two forms:

1. **Intentional** – Disgruntled employees or contractors (current or former)

2. **Accidental** – Authorized employees or contractors making mistakes

Intentional acts related to cybersecurity include the following:

*   Disclosure of sensitive information, such as intellectual property or insider knowledge. An example is the Tesla *Spygate* incident, in which an insider engaged in "quite extensive and damaging sabotage" against the company, including exporting "large amounts of highly sensitive data to unknown third parties."[142]

*   Process corruption, for example, changes to payment approval or user account approval to achieve a larger objective such as theft of funds. An example is a security professional from Facebook who accessed restricted information to stalk women online.[143]

*   Physical or electronic sabotage, such as deletion of databases or manipulation of systems to impact physical processes. Examples include Adam Flanagan of

---

142 Tom Kemp, "What Tesla's Spygate Teaches Us About Insider Threats," *Forbes*, July 19, 2018, accessed June 21, 2021, https://www.forbes.com/sites/forbestechcouncil/2018/07/19/what-teslas-spygate-teaches-us-about-insider-threats/?sh = 4a09507c5afe.

143 Ben Popken, "Facebook Fires Engineer Who Allegedly Used Access to Stalk Women," *NBC News*, May 1, 2018, accessed June 21, 2021, https://www.nbcnews.com/tech/social-media/facebook-investigating-claim-engineer-used-access-stalk-women-n870526.

Pennsylvania, who used his access to radio base stations to disable utility meter reading communications.[144] Vitek Boden, of Maroochydore, Australia, used his access to a sewage treatment control system to release raw sewage into the environment.[145] Both Flanagan and Boden were previously fired from their roles and used their legacy access for revenge.

Accidental acts include the following:

- Physical security failures, such as leaving room or cabinet doors open or unlocked.

- Disclosure of information about systems or projects on social media sites. For example, a vendor's publicity material including details of a customer's system or an individual's LinkedIn profile describing details of that person's role on a project. Either of these could be used in a larger cybersecurity attack.

- Disclosure of account information in a social engineering attack. A common example is the entry of user credentials in response to a phishing email. This can also take place on a telephone call. These attackers often use proprietary information disclosed inappropriately on social media, as described earlier.

- Misconfiguration of systems allowing unauthorized access. Examples include incorrect firewall configuration. This opens external access to a device. Incorrect account configuration enables access to functions or data outside of a user's role.

People management is critical to successful cybersecurity risk reduction. This includes anyone who might be involved, even if they are "invisible."

The Institution of Engineering and Technology (IET) *Draft Code of Practice for Cyber Security in the Built Environment*[146] notes that:

It is important to recognize that the risk from contractors, consultants and agency staff is not confined to those who work in, or have regular physical access to, the built asset. It is becoming increasingly common for technical support to the built asset and its

---

144 Iain Thomson, "US Engineer in the Clink for Wrecking Ex-Bosses' Smart Meter Radio Masts with Pink Floyd lyrics," *The Register*, June 26, 2017, accessed June 21, 2021, https://www.theregister.com/2017/06/26/engineer_imprisoned_for_hacking_exemployer/.

145 Tony Smith, "Hacker Jailed for Revenge Sewage Attacks," *The Register*, October 31, 2001, accessed June 21, 2021, https://www.theregister.com/2001/10/31/hacker_jailed_for_revenge_sewage/.

146 H. Boyes, *Draft Code of Practice for Cyber Security in the Built Environment,* Institution of Engineering and Technology, Version 2.0, January 31, 2021.

operational technology to be provided in part through remote connections by the service engineers and technicians. These largely invisible individuals may have considerable control over these systems and, due to the nature of their work, may be subject to minimal supervision by the organization's own personnel.

Background Checks

Employers need a means of verifying the integrity and honesty of their employees. In general, people with a history of honesty are more likely to be honest in the future. Conversely, applicants who lie to obtain a job are more likely to be dishonest once they have the job. Interviews alone may not be sufficient to weed out dishonest applications.

Background may help. Background checks can verify information such as past employment and education. These checks may involve searching relevant public or private databases, such as driving records, criminal histories, or credit reports. The depth of the background check should be appropriate to the role being filled. Background checks must be conducted in accordance with relevant employment laws. In some jurisdictions, for instance, it is illegal to ask about a criminal record on an application form. For this reason, background checks should be performed by professional and competent individuals or organizations.

As already noted, there can be many individuals involved in operational activities who are not visible to the organization. Some may be working behind the scenes at third-party contractors. Often organizations contract with a third party that then contracts itself with others. This series of relationships may not always be obvious to the original organization. Background checks must be an element of people management. These checks should cover anyone engaged in activities for the organization. Contractual agreements should put the onus of security compliance on the third party for any fourth-tier contractors and should have demonstrable evidence that proper checks have been carried out.

Background checks only help with the initial screening of applicants. Once hired, an employee may fall into substance abuse, debt, or other personal problems. Such difficulties make one vulnerable to acting illegally or unethically. To avoid such risks, some form of ongoing or continuous screening may be required, along with strict oversight.

Separation of Duties

Separation of duties is one means of maintaining employee oversight. Separation of duties involves ensuring that more than one person is required to complete a particular task where safety or security might be at risk. This approach reduces the risk of fraud, theft, and human error. Also known as the *four-eyes principle* (each process involves two people), typical separation of duties may involve the following:

- Separate electronic authorization for particular actions, such as to change set points in a control system or to migrate software between development, testing, and production environments

- The use of multiple security keys (physical or electronic) held by separate personnel

In OT networks, separation of duties can be particularly effective in the management of demilitarized zone (DMZ) firewalls. It is common for organizations to use a single physical firewall to create two logical firewalls. One virtual firewall separates the business network from the DMZ, and the other separates the DMZ from the OT network. In this case, there tends to be one group responsible for configuration and management of the firewall. Any error in one logical firewall could easily be duplicated in the other, creating a significant vulnerability. Using the separation of duties principle, two physical firewalls could be deployed, each managed by a different group. The business network to DMZ firewall could be managed by the IT department, and the DMZ to OT network firewall managed by the OT department. This configuration greatly reduces the likelihood of both firewalls having the same error. The threat of common cause failure could be further reduced by choosing different products for each firewall.

Where it is not possible or practical to separate duties, for example in very small organizations, alternate controls should be in place. These include

- audit trails to track who took what action, and when, and

- periodic supervisory reviews of audit trails and other records to verify all tasks are being performed as expected.

The information recorded in audit trails, and the frequency of reviews should match the level of risk involved. It may be too late to take corrective action if the review frequency is too low. In some cases, the individuals may have left the organization, or the consequences are felt before the cause is known.

Even with the four-eyes principle in place, periodic reviews are essential. In 2005, the US Food and Drug Administration (FDA):

> ...carried out an inspection of Able Laboratories, a New Jersey–based generic pharmaceutical manufacturer between May 2 and July 1, 2005. As a result of finding

discrepancies between paper and electronic records in the analytical laboratory and due to the firm's failure to investigate out-of-specification (OOS) results, the company ceased manufacturing operations, recalled 3,184 batches of product (its entire product line) and withdrew seven Abbreviated New Drug Applications (ANDAs). The resulting problems and a failure to resolve the issue with the FDA resulted in a USD 100 million bankruptcy filing in October 2005 and a fire sale of the company's assets.[147]

Joiners, Movers, and Leavers

Cybersecurity risks begin if people join organizations that lack good security management processes. Such processes start with an information security policy that clearly defines what types of data the organization has and how these types of data are managed. Systems should have owners responsible for approving and monitoring access. These systems should assign user roles at a sufficiently granular level that no person has access to data or functions they do not need to do their job. For example, very few people working in the automation industry need access to accept alarms and even fewer to change alarm limits.

When someone joins an organization, their data access needs should be clear. There should be a formal process to arrange this access. That process should incorporate the four-eyes principle to avoid misuse.

Once someone is in a role, a periodic review process will ensure access is still required. Changes should be made with immediate effect, and records should be kept of the review and any actions arising. Accurate records allow for periodic audits to ensure the processes are being followed.

The greatest risk to any organization is posed by leavers, especially if they are disgruntled. The cases of Adam Flanagan and Vitek Boden, mentioned earlier in this chapter, personify this risk. In both cases, the individuals were fired under acrimonious circumstances. Each of them had administrator-level access to business-critical systems: Flanagan to radio-base stations used by his former company's customer base, including numerous water authorities and sewage treatment plant control systems. Boden stole a laptop containing the control system human-machine interface (HMI) software and a radio. With these, he made at least 46 attempts to turn on sewage pumps between March and April 2000.

Flanagan's unauthorized actions lasted even longer. He was fired in November 2013 and accessed his first base station a few days later (on December 10). His last recorded

---

147 R. D. McDowall, "Quality Assurance Implications for Computerized Systems Following the Able Laboratories FDA Inspection," *Quality Assurance Journal* 10 (2006): 15–20.

unauthorized access of a base station was May 4, 2014. Flanagan and Boden were not sophisticated hackers. In fact, both were caught because they failed to adequately cover their tracks.

Another similar incident occurred in the Netherlands in 2017. Willem Z.,[148] a civil servant of the city of Lopik who was working as manager of the sewage system, was fired in 2016 for integrity violations. Several months later, pumps in the sewage system were started and stopped, valves opened and closed, a specific combination of which could have caused a spill of sewage, damage to pumps or valves, or breaks in sewer pipes. Fortunately, none of this occurred. He also deleted some 8,000 files, preventing remote control of the sewage system for three days. Willem Z. used his employer-provided laptop, which he did not return to the city after being fired, and his knowledge of administrator and individual accounts (including one belonging to a mechanic) to access the systems and data. He also used his administrator credentials to create a test account in an application, unknown to the city's IT department. The files were deleted in November 2016 and January 2017, highlighting again the prolonged period that the disgruntled employee's unauthorized access went unnoticed.[149]

There were many process failures by Flanagan's, Boden's, and Willem Z.'s employers and clients:

- Poor inventory management in the case of Boden and Willem Z. The theft of equipment went undetected in the case of Boden, and Willem Z. was allowed to retain his laptop for many months after he left.

- Poor electronic account management in all cases. Many of the base stations that Flanagan accessed still had their default usernames and passwords. Boden was able to access the control system using existing credentials. Willem Z. used existing administrator credentials to access the systems and create additional, new accounts.

- Poor anomaly and event detection in all cases. In Boden's case, Maroochy Shire Council did not immediately recognize the unauthorized attempts to control the sewage pumps. In Flanagan's case, he modified Kennebec Water District's base station on December 10, 2013, but no one checked the logs until February 2014. In Willem Z.'s case, he deleted files in November 2016 and was able to do the same thing two months later.

---

148 Willem Z.'s full name was not given in any of the online records of this incident.
149 "Sewer Hack Committed Via Admin and Test Accounts" ("Rioolhack gepleegd via admin- en testaccounts"), *AG Connect*, September 14, 2018, accessed June 21, 2021, https://www.agconnect.nl/artikel/rioolhack-gepleegd-admin-en-testaccounts.

The most significant process failure, in all three cases, was the failure to remove access rights and change account details in response to a leaver, in particular, a disgruntled one.

This continues to be a problem, even in large, blue-chip organizations that have the resources to manage risk accordingly. Contractors working at multinational companies continue to have access to business systems for several days, sometimes weeks, after leaving. Rarely, if ever, are user accounts for automation systems changed when someone leaves an organization. Many systems use standard accounts that have been in place for years, or even decades. Former employees of system vendors may still recall the default administrator account for their former company's products.

Manual Procedures

There have been references to manual procedures throughout this book. These range from support processes, such as reviewing and approving access to systems, to system support activities, such as performing backups or operating system patching.

There is a constant push to identify automated methods for performing these procedures. Although automation can be effective in some cases, it is impossible to remove all manual elements. As discussed earlier, continuous oversight and review of activities is critical to avoid malicious activity, fraud, and human error. This type of oversight is resistant to automation.

Manual procedures require documentation. Documentation itself is something that few organizations are good at. Yet well-written, well-maintained documentation is a crucial part of a successful organization. Indeed, it is the hallmark of a well-run organization.

These manual procedures, and their documentation, require time and effort. One reason manual procedures fail is that organizations do not provide the necessary time, resources, and training. With constant pressure to streamline operations, any activity not directly related to profit or productivity is at risk. In many cases, it may be months or years before the effect of these cutbacks is felt. Ironically, organizations that put the time and effort into designing and supporting manual procedures actually become more efficient.

The effort to become agile leads organizations to rethink their processes and procedures. Although many larger organizations could benefit from less bureaucracy, care must be taken to protect critical processes needed to manage business risk, including cybersecurity. If agility is treated as an excuse to remove or short-circuit any and all processes, the result can be chaos.

As a relatively new function, cybersecurity is particularly vulnerable to these issues. In many organizations, individuals who are already fully allocated are given the additional task of *cybersecurity manager, cybersecurity single point of accountability*, or some other function almost as an afterthought. In automation environments, this person might be the lead instrumentation and control technician or engineer in a facility. Although it might make sense for this person to be given responsibility and oversight, he or she will almost certainly need additional resources to ensure the necessary tasks are performed. These resources include the following:

- Operating system and software updates

- Anti-malware updates

- Backups

- User account updates

- Log file analysis

Inventory Management

A key element of successful OT cybersecurity management during operational support is inventory management. When a product vulnerability is announced, the first question to answer is: *Does this affect my organization, and if so, where, and how much?*

It is impossible to answer this question without an accurate and up-to-date equipment inventory. An equipment inventory is sometimes called an *asset register* or *configuration management database*. It can be as simple as an Excel spreadsheet or can be a purpose-made relational database and application. IT and OT security vendors offer inventory management systems.

IT solutions can work well for IT systems and devices. This equipment tends to be based on a small number of standard operating systems, which are normally connected to a network. Most of these cooperate well with asset management systems, providing information about their configuration and patch status, for instance.

The same is not true for OT systems and devices. There are several challenges to using an automated tool to create a reliable OT device inventory:

- The range of device types is much larger and includes many firmware and software solutions that are not designed to interact with asset management solutions.

- Many devices that are networked may only respond to the most basic industrial protocol commands. Rarely do these commands support the return of configuration information. This is a requirement for an effective inventory.

- There is no guarantee that devices are accessible on a common communications network. Many installations will contain serially connected (RS-232, RS-485, RS-422) devices that only respond to the aforementioned basic industrial protocol commands.

- In more modern OT networks, there may be industrial firewalls or data diodes that isolate devices from the wider network. This design limits communications to very few industrial protocol commands.

Some asset owners avoid these issues by focusing their inventories only on *network-connected* devices, or other specific categories such as Windows devices. This strategy is fundamentally flawed. The compromise or failure of any interconnected device could cause operational issues. Every device that is required for the successful operation of the system should be included in the inventory.

Creating an Inventory for New Facilities

For new facilities, creating an inventory should be very straightforward. In all contracts, vendors should be required to provide a specific set of inventory data, such as the following:

- A unique identification number (to make tracking easier, a label with this number should be affixed to the device)

- The manufacturer's make and model number

- Device serial number

- A brief description of the device (e.g., Pump #2 Control PLC, Operator Workstation #1)

- Location of the device (e.g., cabinet number, room number)

- Version number of the device hardware

- A list of all software installed on the device and all associated version numbers

- Any address information (e.g., Internet Protocol address, protocol identifier)

- All configuration and program files for embedded devices such as programmable logic controllers (PLCs) and remote terminal units (RTUs)

- A photograph of the device and where it is installed

This data should be collected as early as possible in the project and maintained throughout the life of the project. It should be treated just like any other controlled document or data source.

Creating an Inventory for Existing Facilities

For existing facilities, creating an inventory is more of a challenge. Automated tools are unlikely to help with the creation of an inventory. The only viable option is to collect the data manually. This is where OT environments have an advantage over IT environments. IT environments may contain hundreds of devices spread over a wide geographic area; and these devices may continually vary in quantity or location. By contrast, OT environments are

- well constrained geographically at known physical locations that never change, and
- limited in quantity and rarely, if ever, change once a system is deployed.

Figure 8-4 shows a breakdown of an OT facility by Windows device (server, workstation, laptop), IT network device (router, switch, wireless access point), OT network device (radio, protocol converter), and embedded device (PLC, RTU).

Figure 8-5 shows how the proportions typically change as the size of the facility increases. Note that as the facility size increases, the number of embedded devices grows, but the number of Windows devices stays relatively fixed. This is because the control room (where most of the Windows devices are located) does not grow in direct proportion to the facility size. The number of embedded devices (PLCs and RTUs) must increase to manage additional process areas.

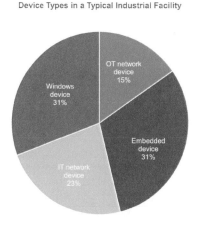

Figure 8-4. Breakdown of device type in a typical OT facility.

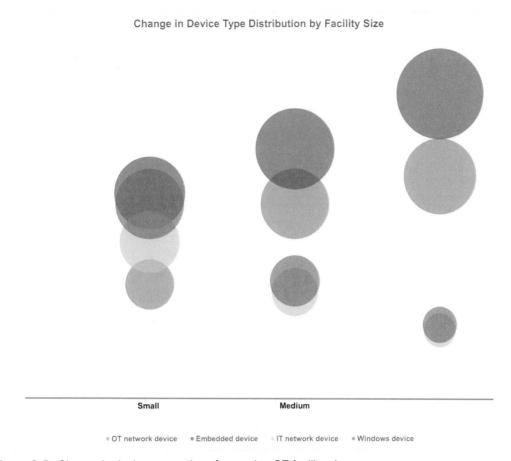

Change in Device Type Distribution by Facility Size

Small   Medium

● OT network device   ● Embedded device   ● IT network device   ● Windows device

Figure 8-5. Change in device proportions for varying OT facility sizes.

This shows that a manual inventory collection is viable. Moreover, if done thoroughly, it will be far more reliable than any automated method of data collection. A thorough data collection process at a typical OT facility will take between one and five days, depending on the size of the facility. As noted earlier, once the inventory data is collected, it is unlikely to change. Therefore, this time investment is minimal over the life of the facility.

All documentation should be reviewed prior to the inventory data collection. Note that documentation should not be relied on for accuracy or completeness. Few organizations adequately maintain their documentation after it is handed over from implementation projects. However, this documentation can provide a good starting point for the data collection. Figure 8-6 shows an example of the type of device that could easily be missed during inventory data collection. In this case, the device (on the left of the photograph) was not shown on any existing documentation. It had been added post-implementation. It was easy to overlook, hidden at the bottom of an equipment rack away from all other equipment. Note that this device would have been overlooked by

Figure 8-6. An easily overlooked device in an operational facility.

any automated inventory tools. It is highly recommended that all documentation is updated after the inventory data collection.

Maintaining and Auditing the Inventory

The inventory must be kept up to date, incorporating changes such as replacement hardware, updated software, changes to addressing, and so on.

Regular audits of inventories and supporting documentation are essential to ensure the following:

- **The data is correct** – Although procedures should require personnel to update the inventory after a change, it is possible for some updates to be missed, or to be made incorrectly. In large systems with many components, it is common to perform a sample inspection of the inventory, checking a percentage of the entries.

- **No unapproved changes have been made** – Although organizations should have a change-management procedure, it is possible for this to be bypassed. For instance, this can occur if the change is perceived as trivial or if the change was made during a system failure where the focus was on returning the system to normal operation.

Personnel who are independent of the system being audited usually undertake these audits. Findings from the audit should be documented and a follow-up scheduled to verify that issues have been addressed.

Incident Response

Incident response planning is not just about preparing for the inevitable incident. Considering plausible scenarios facilitates a review of business risk and the identification of additional mitigations to reduce this risk.

For example, an incident response review identifies that, in the event of a failure or compromise of a particular device requiring replacement (e.g., PLC, network switch), it will take 24 hours to obtain a replacement. The review concludes this downtime will cost the organization more than the expense of holding a spare. As a result, the organization may choose to ensure a spare is available on-site.

Cybersecurity incident response planning is still not universally performed in IT-focused operations. Here is an additional example. In July 2020, Garmin, a provider of sports watches and computers, was the victim of a ransomware attack that prevented users from syncing their data with Garmin's cloud platform. The attackers demanded $10 million. Garmin did not confirm it paid the ransom, but reports indicate the company was forced to.[150] If the only option to recover operations is to pay a ransom, it is clear that there is either no incident response plan in place or the plan was not viable. This could be for one of many reasons, including the following:

- **Failure to identify all plausible scenarios** – This occurs because stakeholders are overly optimistic about their ability to overcome situations, and because there is very little practical experience of dealing with all situations. Incident response plans should consider all plausible scenarios, even those that are extremely unlikely. A low likelihood, high-impact scenario could have serious consequences for an organization that has failed to prepare.

- **Failure to identify all critical systems or components** – This situation is similar to the failure to identify the plausible scenarios. Stakeholders may ignore certain systems or elements because they believe they will not be at risk, or because they have never failed before. Another issue is that the organization has poor inventory management, and the system or component is simply missed.

- **Lack of clear responsibility** – As with cybersecurity in general, there is often too much focus on technical aspects and not enough on people and process. The incident response planning must be realistic about how the organization can recover.

---

150 Alexander Martin, "Garmin Obtains Decryption Key After Ransomware Attack," *Sky News*, July 28, 2020, accessed June 21, 2021, https://news.sky.com/story/garmin-obtains-decryption-key-after-ransomware-attack-12036761.

- **Failure to include all parties** – This is a specific case of the lack of clear responsibility mistake. Very few organizations operate all their systems and facilities themselves. The use of cloud computing and third-party services is common. Incident response plans must include all parties if they are to be effective in the event of an incident.

- **No communication plan** – Many failures of incident management come about because those responsible fail to define a communications plan. Often, they believe the response would be obvious and does not need to be documented. There is no guarantee that the institutional knowledge necessary to recover from an incident will be available when the incident occurs. The communications plan therefore must take account of shift changes, vacations, illness, and change in personnel within the organization and among its stakeholders.

- **No buy-in** – An incident response plan that is written and filed away is useless. Such plans must be developed collaboratively by all stakeholders and address all parties to ensure buy-in.

- **No testing** – The last and most common failure is to not test the incident response plan. Testing is where all the above mentioned issues are on display, and updates to the plan are identified.

Although a failure to plan a viable response to an IT cybersecurity incident can be damaging financially, it can be catastrophic in an OT cybersecurity incident.

On Monday, February 8, 2021, Sheriff Bob Gualtieri of Pinellas County, Florida, gave a press conference in response to the unlawful intrusion to the city of Oldsmar's water treatment system. He was joined by Oldsmar Mayor Eric Seidel and City Manager Al Braithwaite.[151]

During the press conference, Sherriff Gualtieri laid out the sequence of events:

- The operator was aware that his supervisor and other users routinely used remote access to view the HMI screen and so did not report the incident.

- At approximately 1:30 p.m. on the same day, the operator noticed a second remote access to the HMI. This time, the remote user navigated through various screens and eventually modified the set point for sodium hydroxide (lye) to a level that would be toxic to humans.

---

151 "Treatment Plant Intrusion Press Conference," YouTube, accessed June 21, 2021, https://www.youtube.com/watch?v = MkXDSOgLQ6M.

The remote user logged off, and the operator immediately reset the sodium hydroxide level to normal. The operator then disabled remote access and reported the incident to the city and to local and state law enforcement. It is unclear if the operator was following an incident response plan or was just experienced enough to make the right decisions. City representatives stated at the press conference that additional controls were in place to prevent exposure of toxic water to consumers, but they did not describe them in detail.

At the time of this writing, the investigation is still underway, and the culprit, and his or her intentions, remain unclear. The most likely explanations range from an authorized user who made the change in error, a disgruntled former employee or contractor, or a random hacker who discovered the system was accessible from the Internet. Other options that should not be discounted are organized crime syndicates or nation-states. The water treatment plant affected was 15 miles from the Raymond James Stadium in Tampa, Florida, which hosted the Super Bowl just two days after the incident occurred.

It was fortunate that the city of Oldsmar operator was sufficiently observant and aware to take immediate action. This prevented catastrophic consequences. It remains to be seen how well-prepared similar organizations would be.

There are more than 145,000 active public water systems in the United States (including territories). Of these, 97% are considered small systems under the Safe Drinking Water Act, meaning they serve 10,000 or fewer people. Public water systems of the size of the one in the city of Oldsmar (15,000 population) have limited resources to manage threats to their operations.

Although it resulted in a near miss, the Oldsmar incident highlights gaps in process and people elements. Closing these gaps could make future events less likely and the potential consequences less severe:

- The operator observed a remote user several hours before the attempted setpoint adjustment. This did not arouse suspicion because the supervisors used remote access to monitor the plant. Remote access of this type must be strictly limited to specific users, from specific locations, at specific times. The Oldsmar operator should have known who was accessing the system. If this was not an authorized user, it should have prompted the operator to activate the incident response plan. This response would start with disconnecting remote access to the system. It would then initiate various forensics and tests to determine if anything had been altered (e.g., code), in either the systems or processes (e.g., set points, alarms).

- Until the incident was reported, the engineering company that developed the supervisory control and data acquisition (SCADA) system for the city of Oldsmar maintained a page on the portfolio section of its website. This page displayed a screen from the SCADA HMI, providing details of plant processes (e.g., number of reverse osmosis skids, number of pumps on each skid). It was easy to see the button that would enable navigation to the sodium hydroxide page. Such a screenshot is extremely valuable in terms of planning a potential attack. The page is now deleted, although it can be found in Internet archives through search tools.

- The deleted page also had a summary of the project, which included the following description of an automatic control feature: "(Noting that the engineering company…) worked with the city to create an easy-to-use, single-button interface. This button resides on the SCADA screen in the control room and is also accessible through city iPads connected to the SCADA system. Operators can easily press the button to initiate automatic control regardless of their location, which is helpful in emergency situations and during routine site tours." This raises the question about what functionality should be accessible remotely. A common initial reaction to the Oldsmar incident was "There should be no remote access at all, ever." This is unrealistic and impractical. Even if remote access were not available, users would inevitably find their own less secure solutions. This is a cultural issue because the same users would not try to circumvent a safety system or safety procedures. In addition to ensuring remote access is securely designed and limited by user, location, time, and duration, remote access should offer limited functionality. The ability to monitor or view may be all that is required for most users. Although it may be desirable to have an automatic control switch, is it really necessary? In which circumstances would it be used? Are these rare enough that the risk outweighs the benefit?

- The incident raises questions about the functionality of the SCADA system itself. In the aforementioned press conference, the city reported that the unauthorized remote user attempted to change the set point of sodium hydroxide from 100 parts per million (ppm) to 11,100 ppm. This higher level seems to be way outside any normal expected setting. That prompts the question: "Why would the SCADA system accept such a setting?" In fact, it is unclear if it did accept the new level. At the press conference, a city official said the operator reset sodium hydroxide to its normal level, which implies it was changed. Recall the standard layers of protection model that has been presented throughout this book. The basic process control layer's function is to maintain the process within its normal, safe, operating envelope. If this safe operating envelope is not properly defined, the basic process control layer will not perform correctly, which means the risk transfers to other layers, in this case the plant personnel/process alarm layer. Limiting the sodium hydroxide range, restricting who could change it, and from where they could change it would have been significant mitigation factors in this case. This is why OT cybersecurity risk quantification is so different from IT risk quantification. As noted in Chapter 4, the assessment process must consider the hazards in the process and treat cybersecurity as an initiating cause.

Note that many of the incident detection tools and methods promoted by IT vendors (and even some supposed OT vendors) would have done little to help the city of Oldsmar. Intrusion detection and prevention systems only work if the unauthorized access can be identified as abnormal. As already mentioned, even the operator could not determine if the user was authorized. It is unlikely that any tool would have been able to discern this fact. Likewise, regarding the change in the sodium hydroxide set point, if the system enables the user to change the value, then there is no way a detection system could identify this as an anomaly.

The city of Oldsmar incident provides clear evidence of why cybersecurity incident response planning is required, and why this planning must take account of OT factors.

Suppliers, Vendors, and Subcontractors

Asset owners rely heavily on third parties to enable their operations:

- EPC contractors design, build, and operate facilities.

- Cloud environment providers offer platforms to run enterprise systems and store business-critical data.

- Plant equipment providers often sign maintenance contracts that give their employees on-site or remote access to plant performance data.

- Product vendors support systems, meaning their employees have on-site or remote access to those systems.

In many cases, the personnel from these organizations are in place so long that they become indistinguishable from asset-owner personnel. Few asset owners properly manage the cybersecurity risks arising from these arrangements:

- Third-party computers may not have the necessary security controls (e.g., anti-malware protection, application control, user access), yet they may be connected to business-critical systems or networks.

- Vendors may not have sufficient controls in place to manage user credentials for their clients' systems. Examples include having standard administrator accounts for all client systems, sharing account details, and not securely protecting these account details.

- Vendors may not have procedures in place to manage system backups. They must also protect these backups to ensure continuity of operations for their clients. In the case of cloud environment providers, this oversight could be catastrophic for the asset owner, as illustrated by the Blackbaud example earlier in this chapter.

- Suppliers, vendors, and subcontractors may not have adequate security management systems in place in their organization. Their vulnerability to cybersecurity incidents exposes the asset owner.

- Suppliers, vendors, and subcontractors may not provide adequate security awareness training to their personnel. These personnel may be working in the asset owner's business-critical environment where this awareness is essential.

The UK Centre for Protection of National Infrastructure (CPNI) and National Cybersecurity Centre (NCSC) published a set of 12 supply chain principles.[152] These are divided into four stages:

1. Understand the risks:

   a. Understand what must be protected and why.

   b. Know who your suppliers are and build an understanding of what their security looks like.

   c. Understand the security risk posed by your supply chain.

2. Establish control:

   a. Communicate your view of security needs to your suppliers.

   b. Set and communicate minimum security requirements for your suppliers.

   c. Build security considerations into your contracting processes and require that your suppliers do the same.

   d. Meet your own security responsibilities as a supplier and consumer.

---

152 National Cyber Security Centre, "Supply Chain Security Guidance," accessed June 21, 2021, https://www.ncsc.gov.uk/collection/supply-chain-security.

e. Raise awareness of security within your supply chain.

f. Provide support for security incidents.

3. Check your arrangements:

a. Build assurance activities into your approach to managing your supply chain.

4. Implement continuous improvement:

a. Encourage the continuous improvement of security within your supply chain.

b. Build trust with suppliers.

A key step to establishing control is contract management. Contracts should be tailored to specific arrangements. Contract clauses should reflect this. However, to mitigate cyber-security risks, the following key aspects must be included in contracts with third parties:

- Provide a named individual with overall responsibility for cybersecurity and authority to escalate operational security issues or incidents.

- Have an information cybersecurity policy developed in accordance with current industry standards (e.g., NIST [National Institute of Standards and Technology] Framework, ISO 27001/2, ISA/IEC 62443).

- Perform good access control practices:

  o Restrict physical and logical access to sensitive information and systems based on levels of access and privileges required to perform a function or role.

  o Immediately revoke all access for personnel no longer working on the services or those who no longer require access.

  o Review user accounts and privileges on a regular basis to verify that access is correct and remove access that is no longer required.

  o Enforce the use of strong passwords and protect passwords from unauthorized access and interception.

  o Restrict the use of privileged accounts to authorized individuals.

- Provide awareness training to all personnel.

- Protect sensitive information in storage and in transit using encryption. Establish procedures to protect the security of sensitive information at every stage of its life cycle from creation through processing, storage, and disposal.

- Manage end-user devices and servers including malware protection software and patching procedures.

- Report any confirmed security incidents or data breaches promptly and without delay.

- Maintain security incident response plans to manage the response to incidents. Test these plans regularly.

- It should be possible for the contract owner to perform an audit of the third party to ensure it is enforcing the aforementioned practices.

None of these conditions are unreasonable or excessive. Any third party in business today should be doing all these things without contract enforcement. Yet there are many cases where third parties resist some or all of these conditions in contracts. In some instances, those third parties provide unique products or services, and the asset owner feels it has little or no leverage. This is a mistake. Continued acceptance of such gaps reinforces that cybersecurity is not a serious matter. This in turn allows third parties to present a serious risk to the asset owner's operation.

The asset owner should treat these conditions as nonnegotiable. If necessary, such resistance should be escalated to the highest levels in the asset owner and third-party organization. There is no excuse for a failure to employ the most basic cybersecurity controls in businesses of any size.

Insurance

There is an established cyber insurance market focused on IT cybersecurity risks, and insurers and brokers are now developing policies to cover threats to OT infrastructure. As explained in Chapter 2, OT or industrial cybersecurity is different, and insurers and brokers are still learning what risks an asset owner is exposed to from an OT cybersecurity incident. Chapter 4 discussed methods to measure and manage this risk.

The two high-profile ransomware incidents in early 2021 that are referenced in the introduction to this book were resolved when insurers negotiated payments. The asset owners had sufficient insurance coverage to enable payment of large sums ($4.4 million and $11 million).

Tom Finan of Willis Towers Watson, a global insurance broking company, points out that "having a cyber insurance policy does not make a company safer. Instead, an enhanced cybersecurity posture results from going through the cyber insurance application and underwriting process."[153]

Insurance alone is not sufficient for asset owners to manage their IT or OT cybersecurity risk. Asset owners must properly understand and manage their risk if they are to continue to have insurance coverage as part of their overall risk management. As Finan and McIntyre note: "To provide coverage, brokers and underwriters need information about an applicant's cyber risk posture. Brokers seek that information to tell a client's 'story' to the market—specifically, how a client is addressing cyber risk, the lessons it's learned, and how it's applying those lessons. Stories that show steady risk management improvement over time help brokers make an effective case for coverage. For their part, underwriters take on all the risk. In other words, they're the companies that pay out when a bad cyber day happens. Unsurprisingly, they want as much certainty as possible about an applicant's cyber position before they issue a policy."[154]

Summary

Although OT environments have a different operational support culture from IT environments, many factors can give OT cybersecurity the management attention it requires.

- The safety culture that is ingrained in all OT environments can incorporate cybersecurity, treating it as another initiating cause of high-impact incidents that can occur.

- The use of management monitoring tools, such as the barrier representation, can ensure that cybersecurity is considered at the same level as other protective layers.

As noted throughout this book, technology is not the only element of the cybersecurity challenge. People and process are critical weak points. Much of what happens in operational environments revolves around people. Cybersecurity relies on training and awareness, and the adherence to strict processes and procedures. Gaps in training and awareness or in processes and procedures create vulnerabilities that can be as severe as any technical issue.

---

153 Tom Finan and Annie McIntyre, "Cyber Risk and Critical Infrastructure," Willis Towers Watson, March 8, 2021, accessed June 21, 2021, https://www.willistowerswatson.com/en-US/Insights/2021/03/cyber-risk-and-critical-infrastructure.
154 Finan and McIntyre, "Cyber Risk and Critical Infrastructure."

Incident response is one of the most importance plans to have in place. With the growth in high-profile cybersecurity incidents and the knowledge of the costs of dealing with them, it is harder for organizations to ignore the need for good preparation. There is still work to be done to educate asset owners that good incident response planning does not begin and end in their own organization. The use of suppliers, vendors, and subcontractors means that cybersecurity risks, and their remediation, rely on the cooperation of all parties.

One key control that asset owners can use is contract management. A set of model clauses that represent good cybersecurity management should be included in all third-party contracts. These should be nonnegotiable. Any third party that is not already following these practices should not be in business today.

Although insurance can be a useful tool for an asset owner, it cannot replace effective identification and proactive management of risk.

As with all other aspects of cybersecurity management, there is still much to do in operational support, but the elements are in place to improve the cybersecurity posture of all organizations.

9
People, Poetry, and Next Steps

This book is my attempt to address all aspects of industrial cybersecurity. It is based on my own 30-plus years of industrial experience. In all that time, working on projects in various countries and sectors, I am disappointed to see how little has changed. Throughout this book, I have attempted to highlight key issues that are often overlooked. I have deliberately not focused on areas such as network monitoring, penetration testing, and threat analysis. There are many good books that address these and other, more technical, aspects of cybersecurity. My concern is that we are collectively investing hundreds of billions of dollars in technology while failing to address some of our most fundamental nontechnical issues. No business should face a cybersecurity incident because someone failed to remove a former employee's system access or turn a key to the correct position on a safety controller. Businesses will never reach zero risk, but they can reduce the probability of an incident occurring and mitigate the possible consequences. All that's needed is a different perspective.

Understanding the differences between IT and OT cybersecurity, along with quantifying and managing risk, is the foundation of a successful cybersecurity program. With this understanding, one can develop a cybersecurity management system that takes these differences into account.

On the technical side, the foundation of good cybersecurity management is good system design. This book has provided a range of suggestions for defining secure additions and modifications to brownfield sites as well as secure-by-design solutions for greenfield sites.

People and process failures are most apparent in project delivery and operations. Poor execution or oversight can negate some or all the benefits of secure designs. This may occur through the introduction of new vulnerabilities that are not properly identified or addressed. It can surface in the form of poor practices during the development or commissioning of a system.

Raising and maintaining awareness among personnel is key to ensuring that cybersecurity is always at the forefront of everyone's mind. Individual awareness reduces the likelihood of causing an incident and increases the chances of avoiding one.

Cybersecurity is still a long way from being managed like safety. To reach this goal would require the following:

- Secure-by-design systems and products made by companies that recognize the importance of security, even if their customers don't.

- Developers and system integrators trained in the importance of security in their day-to-day work. They must recognize that one mistake could lead to calamity.

- Asset owners who refuse to buy products that are not secure by design and refuse to work with companies that do not demonstrate their commitment to security.

- Facility personnel trained in the importance of security who treat it like safety, as an integral part of their job. This includes stop-work authority if any activity appears insecure.

- The recognition that while technology is an important tool to manage security, it is useless without people and processes.

I will close this book with Don Merrell's revised ending to his famous safety poem "It's Up to Me."[155] It is a reminder to us all that we can, and must, do our part to ensure good cybersecurity management, whether we are product designers, system integrators, engineers, technicians, operators, or managers.

We can all have a workplace that's cyber-incident free
If we each one Commit, to Making It Be,
If we all do our part, and each of us see,
If It's Going to Happen, - Then It's Up to Me.

It is my hope that we will live up to the commitment outlined in this poem.

---

155 Once again, my thanks to Don Merrell for providing this modified verse from his poem "It's Up to Me." It is reprinted with his permission. Contact Don Merrell at donmerrell@hotmail.com to inquire about the use of his poems or to comment on their impact.

Bibliography

Aguilar, Luis A. "Boards of Directors, Corporate Governance, and Cyber-Risks, Sharpening the Focus." Transcript of speech delivered at the Cyber Risks and the Boardroom Conference, New York, NY, June 10, 2014. https://www.sec.gov/news/speech/2014-spch061014laa.

Health and Safety Executive. "ALARP at a glance." Accessed November 6, 2021. https://www.hse.gov.uk/managing/theory/alarpglance.htm.

American National Standards Institute. *Security for Industrial Automation and Control System – Part 1-1: Terminology, Concepts, and Models.* ANSI/ISA-62443-1-1 (99.01.01)–2007. Research Triangle Park, NC: ISA (International Society of Automation).

American National Standards Institute. *Security for Industrial Automation and Control Systems – Part 3-2: Security Risk Assessment for System Design.* ANSI/ISA-62443-3-2-2020. Research Triangle Park, NC: ISA (International Society of Automation).

American National Standards Institute. *Security for Industrial Automation and Control System – Part 3-3: System Security Requirements and Security Levels.* ANSI/ISA-62443-3-3 (99.03.03)-2013. Research Triangle Park, NC: ISA (International Society of Automation).

Barker, Jessica. *Confident Cyber Security.* London: Kogan Page Limited, 2020.

Blackbaud. "Cloud Software Built for the World's Most Inspiring Teams." Accessed June 21, 2021. https://www.blackbaud.com/.

Boyes, H. *Draft Code of Practice for Cyber Security in the Built Environment.* Institution of Engineering and Technology. Version 2.0. January 31, 2021.

Brewster, Thomas. "Warnings as Destructive 'Shamoon' Cyber Attacks Hit Middle East Energy Industry." *Forbes,* December 13, 2018. Accessed June 21, 2021. https://www.forbes.com/sites/thomasbrewster/2018/12/13/warnings-as-destructive-shamoon-cyber-attacks-hit-middle-east-energy-industry/#53fe71893e0f.

Bunge, Jacob. "JBS Paid $11 Million to Resolve Ransomware Attack." *Wall Street Journal,* June 9, 2021. Accessed June 21, 2021. https://www.wsj.com/articles/jbs-paid-11-million-to-resolve-ransomware-attack-11623280781.

Capital Facilities Information Handover Specification, International Association of Oil & Gas Producers (IOGP). "More About CFIHOS." Accessed June 21, 2021. https://www.jip36-cfihos.org/more-about-cfihos/.

Career Onestop Competency Model Clearing House. "Automation Competency Model." Accessed June 21, 2021. https://www.careeronestop.org/competency-model/competency-models/automation.aspx.

Cullen, Lord William. *The Public Inquiry into the Piper Alpha Disaster.* London: Her Majesty's Stationery Office, 1990. http://www.hse.gov.uk/offshore/piper-alpha-disaster-public-inquiry.htm.

"Cybersecurity spending trends for 2022: Investing in the future." CSO. Accessed February 14, 2022. https://www.csoonline.com/article/3645091/cybersecurity-spending-trends-for-2022-investing-in-the-future.html.

Dalakov, George. "The First Computer Virus of Bob Thomas (Complete History)." Accessed July 25, 2021. https://history-computer.com/inventions/the-first-computer-virus-of-bob-thomas-complete-history/.

Disparte, Dante A. "Whaling Wars: A $12 Billion Financial Dragnet Targeting CFOs." *Forbes.* Accessed June 21, 2021. https://www.forbes.com/sites/dantedisparte/2018/12/06/whaling-wars-a-12-billion-financial-dragnet-targeting-cfos/?sh=7d0da85a7e52.

Dragos. "TRISIS Malware: Analysis of Safety System Targeted Malware." Version 1.20171213. Accessed June 21, 2021. https://www.dragos.com/wp-content/uploads/TRISIS-01.pdf.

Duke Energy News Center. "Duke Energy Reaffirms Capital Investments in Renewables and Grid Projects to Deliver Cleaner Energy, Economic Growth." July 5, 2020. Accessed June 21, 2021. https://news.duke-energy.com/releases/releases-20200705-6806042.

Ertan, A., and G. Crossland, C. Heath, D. Denny, and R. Jensen. *Everyday Cyber Security in Organizations*. Royal Holloway: University of London, 2018.

European Union Agency for Cybersecurity (ENISA). "ENISA's Position on the NIS Directive." January 2016. Accessed June 21, 2021. https://www.enisa.europa.eu/publications/enisa-position-papers-and-opinions/enisas-position-on-the-nis-directive.

Evans, Jack. "Someone Tried to Poison Oldsmar's Water Supply during Hack, Sheriff Says." *Tampa Bay Times*, February 9, 2021. Accessed June 21, 2021. https://www.tampabay.com/news/pinellas/2021/02/08/someone-tried-to-poison-oldsmars-water-supply-during-hack-sheriff-says/.

"2017 Equifax Data Breach." Wikipedia. Accessed June 21, 2021. https://en.wikipedia.org/wiki/2017_Equifax_data_breach.

Falliere, N., L. O. Murchu, and E. Chen. *W32.Stuxnet Dossier Version 1.3*. November 2010. Accessed June 21, 2021. https://www.wired.com/images_blogs/threatlevel/2010/11/w32_stuxnet_dossier.pdf.

Finan, T., and A. McIntyre. "Cyber Risk and Critical Infrastructure." Willis Towers Watson website. March 8, 2021. Accessed June 21, 2021. https://www.willistowerswatson.com/en-US/Insights/2021/03/cyber-risk-and-critical-infrastructure.

Finances Online "119 Impressive Cybersecurity Statistics: 2020/2021 Data & Market Analysis." Accessed June 21, 2021. https://financesonline.com/cybersecurity-statistics/.

"FireEye Responds to Wave of Destructive Cyber Attacks in Gulf Region." FireEye (blog). December 1, 2016. Accessed June 21, 2021. https://www.fireeye.com/blog/threat-research/2016/11/fireeye_respondsto.html.

Fortinet. "FortiGate® 7000E Series FG-7060E, FG-7040E, and FG-7030E Datasheet." Accessed June 28, 2021. https://www.fortinet.com/content/dam/fortinet/assets/data-sheets/FortiGate_7000_Series_Bundle.pdf.

Fortum. "Siemens Carried Out First Remote Start-Up and Adjustment Work in Russia at Nyagan GRES." Accessed June 21, 2021. https://www.fortum.com/media/2020/06/siemens-carried-out-first-remote-start-and-adjustment-work-russia-nyagan-gres.

"Gartner Forecasts Worldwide Security and Risk Management Spending to Exceed $150 Billion in 2021." Gartner. May 17, 2021. Accessed June 21, 2021. https://www.gartner.com/en/newsroom/press-releases/2021-05-17-gartner-forecasts-world-wide-security-and-risk-managem.

Geller, E. S. "10 Leadership Qualities for a Total Safety Culture." *Professional Safety*, May 2020. Accessed June 21, 2021. http://campus.murraystate.edu/academic/faculty/dfender/OSH650/readings/Geller—10%20Leadership%20Qualities%20for%20a%20Total%20Safety%20Culture.pdf.

Gruhn, Paul. "Bayesian Analysis Improves Functional Safety." *InTech*, March 31, 2020. Accessed June 21, 2021. https://www.isa.org/intech-home/2020/march-april/features/bayesian-analysis-improves-functional-safety.

Hemmerdinger, Jon. "Boeing Asked FAA in 2017 to Strip MCAS from Max Training Report." FlightGlobal (website), October 18, 2019. Accessed June 21, 2021. https://www.flightglobal.com/airframers/boeing-asked-faa-in-2017-to-strip-mcas-from-max-training-report/134896.article.

Henriquez, Maria. "Blackbaud Sued After Ransomware Attack." *Security* magazine, November 6, 2020. Accessed June 21, 2021. https://www.securitymagazine.com/articles/93857-blackbaud-sued-after-ransomware-attack.

Hubbard, Douglas W., and R. Seiersen. *How to Measure Anything in Cybersecurity Risk.* Hoboken, NJ: John Wiley & Sons, 2016.

Hopkinson, Martin. "Monte Carlo Schedule Risk Analysis—A Process for Developing Rational and Realistic Risk Models." White paper, Risk Management Capability, 2011. Accessed June 21, 2021. http://www.rmcapability.com/resources/Schedule + Risk + Analysis + v1.pdf.

International Organization for Standardization and International Electrotechnical Commission. *Information Technology – Security techniques — Information security management systems — Requirements.* ISO/IEC 27001:2013. Geneva 20, Switzerland.

Information Commissioner's Office. "The Guide to NIS." Accessed June 21, 2021. https://ico.org.uk/for-organisations/the-guide-to-nis.

International Electrotechnical Commission. *Functional Safety of Electrical/Electronic/Programmable Electronic Safety-Related Systems – Part 1: General Requirements.* IEC 61508-1:2010. Geneva 20, Switzerland.

International Electrotechnical Commission. *Enterprise-Control System Integration.* IEC 62264-1:2013. Geneva 20, Switzerland.

"Industry 4.0." University of West Florida (website). Accessed June 21, 2021. https://uwf.edu/centers/haas-center/industrial-innovation/industry-40/.

IBM X-Force Threat Intelligence Index 2020, 8. IBM Security. Accessed June 21, 2021. https://www.scribd.com/document/451825308/ibm-x-force-threat-intelligence-index-2020-pdf.

Jewkes, S., and J. Finkle. "Saipem Says Shamoon Variant Crippled Hundreds of Computers." Reuters, December 12, 2018. Accessed June 21, 2021. https://www.reuters.com/article/us-cyber-shamoon/saipem-says-shamoon-variant-crippled-hundreds-of-computers-idUSKBN1OB2FA.

Kahneman, Daniel. *Thinking, Fast and Slow.* New York: Farrar, Straus and Giroux, 2011.

Kemp, Tom. "What Tesla's Spygate Teaches Us About Insider Threats." *Forbes.* Accessed June 21, 2021. https://www.forbes.com/sites/forbestechcouncil/2018/07/19/what-teslas-spygate-teaches-us-about-insider-threats/?sh = 4a09507c5afe.

Krigman, Amy. "Cyber Autopsy Series: Ukrainian Power Grid Attack Makes History." GlobalSign Blog. October 22, 2020. Accessed June 21, 2021. https://www.globalsign.com/en/blog/cyber-autopsy-series-ukranian-power-grid-attack-makes-history.

Langer, Ralph. *To Kill a Centrifuge: A Technical Analysis of What Stuxnet's Creators Tried to Achieve.* Accessed June 21, 2021. Arlington, VA: The Langner Group. November 2013. https://www.langner.com/wp-content/uploads/2017/03/to-kill-a-centrifuge.pdf.

Lucchini, S. "I Thought I Had the Right Roadmap for Implementing a Safety System!" White paper, Texas A&M Engineering Experiment Station, 20th Annual International Symposium, Mary Kay O'Connor Process Safety Center, Texas A&M University, 2017.

Lockheed Martin Corporation. "The Cyber Kill Chain." Accessed June 21, 2021. https://www.lockheedmartin.com/en-us/capabilities/cyber/cyber-kill-chain.html.

Martin, Alexander. "Garmin Obtains Decryption Key After Ransomware Attack." *Sky News*, July 28, 2020. Accessed June 21, 2021. https://news.sky.com/story/garmin-obtains-decryption-key-after-ransomware-attack-12036761.

Marszal, E., and J. McGlone. *Security PHA Review for Consequence-Based Cybersecurity.* Research Triangle Park, NC: ISA (International Society of Automation), 2019.

McCoy, Kevin. "Target to Pay $18.5M for 2013 Data Breach that Affected 41 Million Consumers." *USA Today*. Updated May 23, 2017. Accessed June 21, 2021. https://www.usatoday.com/story/money/2017/05/23/target-pay-185m-2013-data-breach-affected-consumers/102063932/.

McGee, Marianne Kolbasuk. "Blackbaud Ransomware Breach Victims, Lawsuits Pile Up." BankInfo Security, Information Security Media Group, September 24, 2020. Accessed June 21, 2021. https://www.bankinfosecurity.com/blackbaud-ransomware-breach-victims-lawsuits-pile-up-a-15053.

McDowall, R. D. "Quality Assurance Implications for Computerized Systems Following the Able Laboratories FDA Inspection." *Quality Assurance Journal* 10 (2006): 15–20.

McLeod, Dr. Saul. "Maslow's Hierarchy of Needs." Updated December 29, 2020. Accessed June 21, 2021. https://www.simplypsychology.org/maslow.html.

Mustard, Steve. *Mission Critical Operations Primer.* Research Triangle Park, NC: ISA (International Society of Automation), 2018.

The Mitre Corporation. "ATT&CK for Industrial Control Systems." Accessed June 21, 2021. https://collaborate.mitre.org/attackics/index.php/Main_Page.

Nakashima, E., Y. Torbati, and W. Englund. "Ransomware Attack Leads to Shutdown of Major US Pipeline System." *Washington Post*, May 8, 2021. Accessed June 21, 2021. https://www.washingtonpost.com/business/2021/05/08/cyber-attack-colonial-pipeline/.

National Cyber Security Centre (NCSC). "Supply Chain Security Guidance." Accessed June 21, 2021. https://www.ncsc.gov.uk/collection/supply-chain-security.

National Cyber Security Centre (NCSC). "NIS Compliance Guidelines for Operators of Essential Service (OES)." Accessed June 21, 2021. https://www.ncsc.gov.ie/pdfs/NIS_Compliance_Security_Guidelines_for_OES.pdf.

NIST. "Components of the Cybersecurity Framework." Presentation, July 2018. https://www.nist.gov/cyberframework/online-learning/components-framework.

North Carolina State University and Protiviti. "Illuminating the Top Global Risks in 2020." Accessed June 21, 2021. https://www.protiviti.com/US-en/2020-top-risks.

"Order Granting Final Approval of Settlement, Certifying Settlement Class, and Awarding Attorney's Fees, Expenses, and Service Awards." Equifax Data Breach Settlement. Accessed June 21, 2021. https://www.equifaxbreachsettlement.com/admin/services/connectedapps.cms.extensions/1.0.0.0/927686a8-4491-4976-bc7b-83cccaa34de0_1033_EFX_Final_Approval_Order_(1.13.2020).pdf.

Occupational Health and Safety Hub. "Quick Safety Observation Card – Free Template." https://ohshub.com/quick-safety-observation-card-free-template/.

Pauli, Darren. "Barbie-Brained Mattel Exec Phell for Phishing, Sent $3m to China." *The Register*, April 6, 2016. Accessed May 12, 2022. https://www.theregister.com/2016/04/06/chinese_bank_holiday_foils_nearperfect_3_million_mattel_fleecing.

Popken, Ben. "Facebook Fires Engineer Who Allegedly Used Access to Stalk Women." NBC News, May 1, 2018. Accessed June 21, 2021. https://www.nbcnews.com/tech/social-media/facebook-investigating-claim-engineer-used-access-stalk-women-n870526.

POSC Caesar Association. "An Introduction to ISO 15926." November 2011. Accessed June 21, 2021. https://www.posccaesar.org/wiki/ISO15926Primer.

Prince, Brian. "Researchers Detail Critical Vulnerabilities in SCADA Product." *Security Week*, March 13, 2014. Accessed June 21, 2021. https://www.securityweek.com/researchers-detail-critical-vulnerabilities-scada-product.

Rathwell, Gary. PERA Enterprise Integration (website). Accessed June 21, 2021. http://www.pera.net/.

RSAC Contributor. "The Future of Companies and Cybersecurity Spending." Accessed June 21, 2021. https://www.rsaconference.com/library/Blog/the-future-of-companies-and-cybersecurity-spending.

RiskBased Security. "2020 Year End Report: Data Breach QuickView." Accessed June 21, 2021. https://pages.riskbasedsecurity.com/en/en/2020-yearend-data-breach-quickview-report.

Reason, James. "Achieving a Safe Culture: Theory and Practice." *Work & Stress: An International Journal of Work, Health and Organisations* 12, no. 3 (1998): 302. Accessed June 21, 2021. https://www.tandfonline.com/doi/abs/10.1080/02678379808256868.

Schneier, Bruce. "Secrets and Lies: Introduction to the Second Edition." Schneier on Security (blog). Accessed June 21, 2021. https://www.schneier.com/books/secrets-and-lies-intro2.

Sanger, David E., N. Perlroth, and E. Schmitt. "Scope of Russian Hack Becomes Clear: Multiple U.S. Agencies Were Hit." *New York Times,* December 14, 2020. Accessed June 21, 2021. https://www.nytimes.com/2020/12/14/us/politics/russia-hack-nsa-homeland-security-pentagon.html.

"Sewer Hack Committed Via Admin and Test Accounts" ("Rioolhack gepleegd via admin- en testaccounts"). *AG Connect,* September 14, 2018. Accessed June 21, 2021. https://www.agconnect.nl/artikel/rioolhack-gepleegd-admin-en-testaccounts.

Shaw, William T. *Cybersecurity for SCADA Systems.* Tulsa, OK: PennWell Corporation, 2006.

Smith, Rebecca. "Duke Energy Broke Rules Designed to Keep Electric Grid Safe." *Wall Street Journal.* Updated February 1, 2019. Accessed June 21, 2021. https://www.wsj.com/articles/duke-energy-broke-rules-designed-to-keep-electric-grid-safe-11549056238.

Smith, Tony. "Hacker Jailed for Revenge Sewage Attacks." *The Register,* October 31, 2001. Accessed June 21, 2021. https://www.theregister.com/2001/10/31/hacker_jailed_for_revenge_sewage/.

Spitzner, Lance. "Security Awareness Maturity Model." Blog, January 1, 2019. Accessed June 21, 2021. https://www.sans.org/security-awareness-training/blog/security-awareness-maturity-model/.

"S.I. No. 360/2018 – European Union (Measures for a High Common Level of Security of Network and Information Systems) Regulations 2018." Electronic *Irish Statute Book.* Accessed June 21, 2021. http://www.irishstatutebook.ie/eli/2018/si/360/made/en.

SP 800-82 Rev. 2. *Guide to Industrial Control Systems (ICS) Security.* Gaithersburg, MD: NIST (National Institute of Standards and Technology), 2015. Accessed June 21, 2021. https://csrc.nist.gov/publications/detail/sp/800-82/rev-2/final.

"Summary Report of Audits Performed by Netherland, Sewell & Associates." Accessed June 21, 2021. https://www.sec.gov/Archives/edgar/data/101778/00011931251004 2898/dex992.htm.

Sugarman, E., and H. Wickline. "The Sorry State of Cybersecurity Imagery." Hewlett Foundation website, July 25, 2019. https://hewlett.org/ the-sorry-state-of-cybersecurity-imagery/.

Thomson, Iain. "US Engineer in the Clink for Wrecking Ex-Bosses' Smart Meter Radio Masts with Pink Floyd lyrics." *The Register*, June 26, 2017. Accessed June 21, 2021. https://www.theregister.com/2017/06/26/engineer_imprisoned_for_ hacking_exemployer/.

Thompson, Mark. "Iranian Cyber Attack on New York Dam Shows Future of War." *Time*, March 24, 2016. Accessed June 21, 2021. https://time.com/4270728/ iran-cyber-attack-dam-fbi/.

Thaler, Richard H., and C. R. Sunstein. *Nudge: Improving Decisions About Health, Wealth, and Happiness*. New Haven, CT: Yale University Press, 2008.

"Treatment Plant Intrusion Press Conference." YouTube. Accessed June 21, 2021. https://www.youtube.com/watch?v=MkXDSOgLQ6M.

Tofino. "Argon Security Appliance Data Sheet." DS-TSA-ARGON, Version 5.0. Accessed June 28, 2021. https://www.tofinosecurity.com/sites/default/files/DS-TSA-ARGON.pdf.

Vazquez, J., and J. Vilas. "A patadas con mi SCADA! [Rooted CON 2014]." YouTube. Accessed June 21, 2021. https://www.youtube.com/watch?v=oEwxm8EwtYA&lis t=PLUOjNfYgonUsrFhtONP7a18451psKNv4I&index=23.

Williams, Theodore J. *The Purdue Enterprise Reference Architecture: A Technical Guide for CIM Planning and Implementation*. Research Triangle Park, NC: Instrument Society of America, 1992.

Warrick, J., and E. Nakashima. "Officials: Israel Linked to a Disruptive Cyberattack on Iranian Port Facility." *Washington Post*, May 18, 2020. Accessed June 21, 2021. https://www.washingtonpost.com/national-security/officials-israel-linked-to-a-disruptive-cyberattack-on-iranian-port-facility/2020/05/18/9d1da866-9942-11ea-89fd-28fb313d1886_story.html.

World Nuclear Association. "Chernobyl Accident 1986." Updated April 2022. https://www.world-nuclear.org/information-library/safety-and-security/safety-of-plants/chernobyl-accident.aspx.

Young, Chris. "A 22-Year-Old Logged in and Compromised Kansas's Water System Remotely." Interesting Engineering (website), April 6, 2021. Accessed June 21, 2021. https://interestingengineering.com/a-22-year-old-logged-in-and-compromised-kansas-water-system-remotely.

Appendix A:
Resources

Further Reading

Barker, Jessica. *Confident Cyber Security: How to Get Started in Cyber Security and Futureproof Your Career.* London: Kogan Page Limited, 2020, ISBN 978-1789663426.

Hubbard, Douglas W. and Seiersen, Richard. *How to Measure Anything in Cybersecurity Risk.* Hoboken, NJ: John Wiley & Sons, Inc., 2016.

Marszal, Edward, and McGlone, Jim. *Security PHA Review for Consequence-Based Cybersecurity.* Research Triangle Park, NC: ISA (International Society of Automation), 2019.

Langer, Ralph. "To Kill A Centrifuge: A Technical Analysis of What Stuxnet's Creators Tried to Achieve." Arlington, VA: The Langner Group, November 2013. Accessed June 21, 2021. https://www.langner.com/wp-content/uploads/2017/03/to-kill-a-centrifuge.pdf.

Mustard, Steve. *Mission Critical Operations Primer.* Research Triangle Park, NC: ISA (International Society of Automation), 2018.

Williams, Theodore J. *The Purdue Enterprise Reference Architecture: A Technical Guide for CIM Planning and Implementation.* Research Triangle Park, NC: Instrument Society of America, 1992. ISBN 1556172656, 9781556172656.

"TRISIS Malware: Analysis of Safety System Targeted Malware." Version 1.20171213. Dragos, Inc. Accessed June 21, 2021. https://www.dragos.com/wp-content/uploads/TRISIS-01.pdf.

Useful Resources

Infracritical (http://infracritical.com/). Infracritical is an organization founded by Bob Radvonsky, Jake Brodksy, Tammy Olk, and Michael Smith, internationally recognized experts in the field of industrial cybersecurity. Infracritical provides two resources:

- The Systems and Cyber Impact Database Markup (SCIDMARK), which is available at http://search.infracritical.com/. This site provides a register of industrial cybersecurity incidents.

- The SCADASec mailing list. This free service enables individuals to share knowledge and discuss industrial cybersecurity issues with experts around the world.

Top 20 secure PLC coding practices (https://www.plc-security.com/). This project provides guidelines for engineers who are creating software used in industrial control systems.

International Society of Automation, ISA (https://isa.org). ISA's ISA99 standards committee develops and maintains the ISA/IEC 62443 Series of Standards, the only international standards for the security of industrial automation and control systems. ISA also offers training courses and a certificate program for industrial cybersecurity, as well as read-only access to the ISA/IEC 62443 series of standards for society members.

ISA Global Cybersecurity Alliance, ISAGCA (https://isaautomation.isa.org/cybersecurity-alliance/). This collaborative forum was established to advance cybersecurity awareness, education, readiness, and knowledge sharing. Membership is open to any organization involved in industrial cybersecurity: end users, automation providers, system integrators, consultants, and government agencies.

ISA Security Compliance Institute, ISCI (https://www.isasecure.org). The ISCI functions as an operational group within ISA's Automation Standards Compliance Institute.

The institute provides market awareness, technical support, education, and compliance for the ISASecure industrial automation control system (IACS) security requirements that are based on ISA/IEC 62443.

Dale Peterson (https://dale-peterson.com). Dale Peterson is the founder of the security consulting firm Digital Bond and the S4 conference. He is an industrial control systems cybersecurity evangelist, and his blog posts and podcasts provide excellent resources for those in the profession.

Ralph Langner (https://www.langner.com/). Ralph Langner is recognized for his comprehensive analysis of the Stuxnet malware and is considered a leading expert in industrial control systems cybersecurity. His company's website provides a wide variety of resources for those in the profession.

Dragos (https://www.dragos.com/). Founded by Rob Lee, a former US Air Force Cyber Warfare Operations Officer and r enowned industrial cybersecurity e xpert, Dragos regularly provides detailed analysis of high-profile incidents such as TRISIS. The Dragos website is an excellent resource for those in the profession.

PERA Enterprise Integration (http://www.pera.net/). Gary Rathwell, one of the members of the team that developed the original Purdue Enterprise Reference Architecture (PERA), maintains a website to continue the development of this essential reference model.

(CS)²AI (https://www.cs2ai.org/), founded by Derek Harp and Bengt Gregory-Brown, is a global, not-for-profit, workforce-development organization supporting professionals of all levels charged with securing control systems. They provide a platform for members to help members foster meaningful peer-to-peer exchange, continue professional education, and directly support cybersecurity professional development.

Index

Note: "n" refers to the footnote.